CONTENTS

Illustrations by
John Leeder, David Brian,
David Fryer and Stephen Livesey

Edited by M. Broadley

Copyright © MCMLXX by
World Distributors (Manchester) Limited
All rights reserved throughout the world

Published in Great Britain by
World Distributors (Manchester) Limited
P.O. Box 111, 12 Lever Street,
Manchester M60 1TS
Printed and bound in England by
Jarrold & Sons Ltd, Norwich

SBN 7235 0080 0

A STORY OF COURAGE

By Stephen Andrews

We were talking about courage in general when old Jeff Chambers told me a story that licked any I ever heard, either before or since

As a sports writer I get around. I meet all sorts of champions, and I make it my business to find out what makes them tick. All of them I know have one thing in common: they are all dedicated to their particular sport. Knowing what I know now, I reckon I could have been a champion, had I not wasted my time hanging around street corners when I was a youth. Even so, I can still play a pretty good game of football, on the wing, and at golf I can beat many who have had more practice at the game than I'll ever have.

But there is one sport which leaves me excited and numb at the same time, and that is high-diving. The sheer nerve of the high divers sets my hair on end. I cannot imagine how, though I've seen them do it, the divers, many of them youngsters just out of school, can hurl themselves off a board higher than a couple of double-decker buses, turn in the air with superb precision and plunge into the water with hardly a splash.

No, sir, no coach in the world could have made a high diver out of me. I get a touch of the collywobbles when I stand by the side of a duck-pond. But I like the sport and, as I've said before, I find it exciting, so when my paper asked me to report on the recent British Commonwealth Games, held this year in Western Australia, I jumped at the chance.

Many of the young divers were new to me, of course, I didn't even know their names, though the faces of some of the coaches and officials were familiar.

It was in the spectators' enclosure by the high diving pool where I saw my old pal, Jeff Chambers. He won an Olympic gold medal, swimming the 100 metres for Australia in 1948. Since I had last seen him, he had had a tussle with a shark and had lost his right leg. However, he didn't let it get him down; since then he had done a bit of tuna fishing in the Indian Ocean.

It wasn't long before we were cheerfully swapping yarns about the good old days.

I happened to remark how much I admired the courage of the young high divers who were competing in the games. In fact, we were talking about courage in general when old Jeff Chambers told me a story that licked any I ever heard, either before or since. Being a writer I was able to reconstruct the story as it probably happened, but I must point out that I cannot take the credit for inventing it or having taken any part in it.

As I've said before, this is a story of courage. It starts in the town of Wooluminbah, on the north-west coast of Australia.

It's a hot place, especially in the summers, and during the lunch break the kids used to play in the cool waters of Flint Creek.

One day, a bunch of outback kids were playing about in the river near the river bank. They used to get up to all sorts of tricks and have a whale of a time. The kids were mostly between the ages of nine and fourteen, and as their school was on the river bank, it was very handy for them to

and succeeded only in making a splash. Since he had broken his leg he had completely lost his confidence to swim, and he knew it. He would pull himself out of the water dejectedly and watch Ned Norcross make his spectacular racing dives into the water. Splash envied all his pals, but especially Ned Norcross.

So well did his pals take to the water that Splash felt uneasy in their company, so he used to wander off a little distance away, to a pier which jutted out into the creek, where he could be near enough to watch his pals, but far enough away not to have to listen to their jibes. They called him "the human submarine" or "the go-nowhere paddle-steamer". The only real pal he had at that time was a little mongrel pup called 'Pops', which used to hang around the school.

The pier had been out of use for years, as long as he could remember. The timbers were rotten, so it wasn't surprising when Splash dislodged one of the planks accidentally. Unfortunately, this threw Pops off balance, and the pup fell off the pier.

Splash looked down and saw Pops struggling to keep its head above the swirling eddies. Not knowing how deep the water was at that point, Splash dare not go in, although he desperately wanted to save the pup.

"Hold on, Pops, I'll get help," he said, and he turned his back on the pup.

Splash ran along the river bank to his pals in the water, trying to ignore the barking of the pup in his ears. He felt ashamed. He felt worthless. He knew he was a coward.

"Help, help!" he yelled, pointing back to the pier. "Pops has fallen into the river."

Ned Norcross, the school champion, raced to the rescue. He cut through the water towards the pier like a shark. He grabbed the pup by the scruff of the neck and held it out of the water. He stood up, showing that the water only came up to his neck. The other kids ran along the pier to lend a hand. One of them reached down for the pup.

"Well done, Ned. You saved Pops."

"The pup nearly drowned," said Ned, climbing onto the pier. He grabbed Splash by the hair. "Mutton-

nip out for a dip when they had the time.

Like Australian kids in general, every kid in the school could swim like a fish, except Bill Waters, who was spitefully nicknamed 'Splash' by Ned Norcross, the best swimmer in the school.

Splash Waters was a tall, but thin, schoolboy of about thirteen. He had a rugged, determined expression, and although he had broken his leg as an infant, he looked as healthy as the other kids.

He used to play about in the river. He tried to learn to swim the crawl, but although he put a lot of energy into his efforts, he had no rhythm

head! You should have gone in after Pops."

"I . . . I can't swim properly," stuttered Splash, breaking away.

"The water's only five feet deep, Yellowguts!"

Splash walked down the pier with hunched shoulders, trying to ignore the cat-calls of his pals. He was relieved, of course, that the pup had been saved, but the jibes hurt, because he knew they were true. Not only could he not swim, but near the water he was a coward.

The jibes cut deep and they still bothered him so much that he was determined to show his pals one day what he could do.

So that night, Splash returned to the pier. There was a good moon and he found his way to the edge of the pier without trouble. There he undressed. He stood on the edge of the pier and prepared to leap into the black waters.

"I've got to prove I'm not a coward," he said.

He licked his lips and leapt off the pier. He had passed the point of no return. But the tide had come in and the current caught him and dragged him into midstream. He struggled in the dark waters to remain afloat.

I've lost my foothold. Help! I'm out of my depth, thought Splash.

It was more by good luck than by his own efforts that Splash kept his head above water. He was almost swept out to sea, but good fortune was with him, because at that time Jeff Chambers was returning to the creek in his fishing smack.

"Help!"

Jeff was at the helm and immediately manoeuvred his craft to the boy in trouble. He stuck out his boathook, which Splash clutched desperately.

"You saved my life," said Splash, as he was pulled aboard.

But the old fisherman could not condone the youngster's irresponsibility. "What are you doing out here at this time of night? You're out of your mind, kid."

Splash did not argue. He was grateful that he had been saved, but he was even more hurt by his repeated failures. By the time he had been returned home safely he was determined that he would learn to swim. It was the only way he would be able to overcome his sense of inferiority.

In his bedroom he lay across his bedside chair and practised his swimming strokes, referring to an open book on the subject, on the floor.

"Kick . . . Two . . . Three . . . Blow. . ." he called out, long into the night.

After that he practised swimming in the creek in the early mornings, before he met his pals. Such perseverance was bound to pay off in the long run, and eventually he taught himself to swim without touching the bottom.

"Kick . . . Two . . . Three . . . Breathe . . . I am swimming," he shouted out in delight. "Now I'll practise every day until I can beat Ned Norcross."

With this dream in mind, Splash

practised every day by swimming half a mile down the creek to school. He progressed steadily, though rather slowly.

But Splash's progress was noticed. He thought no one had seen him in the river in the early mornings, although he frequently passed Jeff's fishing smack moored in the creek.

Although the old-timer had thought the youngster had acted irresponsibly that first night, he was impressed by the youngster's determination. He had noted that the lad had never missed an early morning swim for a month.

Then, one morning, Splash was startled to hear a stranger in the water beside him. He half-turned to see the old-timer, stripped to the waist, swimming just behind him.

"Last one to the pier is a cissy," said Jeff.

Splash accepted the challenge. He raced through the water as fast as he could to hold onto his half-a-yard lead, and just reached the pier first.

"Beat you!"

Splash climbed up onto the pier and helped the old man up after him. "You're . . . you're the fisherman who saved my life a month ago, aren't you?"

Jeff nodded. He pushed his hand into his denim pocket and pulled out a medal.

"You swim pretty well for an old man with one leg, if you don't mind me saying so," said Splash. "Had I known about your leg, I mean, I wouldn't have raced you. I don't want to hurt your feelings."

Jeff laughed and gave the medal to the boy. "I promised to give this medal to the first man to beat me over 100 metres."

"But that's not fair on you." Splash looked at the medal. "Wow! Are you Jeff Chambers, the Olympic Champion?"

Splash sat on the pier and stared at the medal. The old timer put his hand on the boy's shoulder. "I was, in 1948. You've got guts, kid, and that's what it takes to make a champion. I'd like to show you how to win a swimming gold for Australia, if you'd let me."

"Just show me how to beat Ned Norcross, Mr. Chambers!"

With such an enthusiastic apprentice and an experienced coach, progress was inevitable. Every evening Splash used to go out to sea with Jeff, in the fishing smack, to give him a hand with his catch. Then, when they had sufficient tuna in the hold, Jeff would turn his helm for home. Splash would leap into the water and swim alongside the smack to the creek. Jeff would stay on deck to warn the youngster at the first sight of any shark.

Jeff had a good eye for a swimmer and he noted that Splash, although he swam with great determination, used his energy in his strokes instead of against the water. In fact the youngster was fighting himself rather than the sea. He had reached the point where he could not improve his performance.

So the next evening, Jeff pretended to have engine trouble. "Looks like we have to spend the night drifting out here," he said casually.

Splash sat on the deck and gazed into the water.

"Mind you," went on Jeff, "if I had both my legs, I would take a line round my shoulders and tow the smack back to the creek."

Splash raised his eyebrows. "Is that possible? This boat must weigh over five tons, and it's over a mile to the creek."

Jeff lit his pipe. "It's surprising how easy it is to move even a big boat through the water."

Splash frowned. He picked up a line and looked at it for a minute. He licked his lips. "I'll give it a try," he said, and slipped a loop around his body.

Splash went over the side and started swimming. Painfully slowly he moved the boat behind him. No longer dare he concentrate his energy perfecting his swimming strokes. He had to pit all his strength against the sea.

Three hours later he dragged the boat into the mouth of the creek. Jeff switched on the boat's engines. "Climb aboard, boy," he said. "I reckon you've earned yourself a ride up the creek."

Splash was almost speechless as he was pulled out of the water. "I thought the engine had broken down," he spluttered.

Jeff smiled. "Let's see how you can swim tomorrow," he said simply.

Splash had not the energy left to argue.

In the following weeks, Splash improved rapidly. In a practise swim, he covered a mile in eighteen minutes. Jeff leapt for joy.

"You've broken the school record, boy-oh! You can now whack Ned Norcross anytime you want."

Splash lay on the deck on the fishing smack and gazed up at the sky. Jeff sat down beside him.

"Now, how about entering for this year's Western Australian championship?" suggested Jeff. "I reckon with a little more training you stand a good chance of winning even that."

Splash smiled. "No thanks, Mr. Chambers. I've done all the swimming I set out to do. I owe you a lot, but I've achieved everything I want now."

"But, but . . ." spluttered Jeff. "You can't turn your back on swimming now! You've got the makings of an

Olympic champion. In the next Olympics you could win a gold for Australia."

Splash smiled. "I'm not really interested, Mr. Chambers. When I took up swimming, it was not to win a medal. All I was trying to do was to prove myself, that's all, and now I've done just that."

"But, but, there's no need to give up swimming altogether . . ."

Splash stood up and smiled. "I can't see much point in going on, if my heart's not in it." He held out his hand. "Thank you for all you've done for me, Mr. Chambers. You've helped me more than you can ever know. You have helped me to fight my own fear. You have given me back my courage."

"Ah, piffle," said Jeff in disgust. "Now listen here, boy-oh. I want you down here tomorrow evening for another spell of training."

Splash smiled. He shook hands with his coach and left the fishing smack. From that day onwards, he

never swam more than a dozen strokes.

The spectators' enclosure around the high diving pool was now crowded as the main high diving events were about to begin.

"You mean that boy turned his back on swimming?" I said. "Even though he had it in him to be a champion?"

Jeff nodded. "From that day to this I don't think he ever attempted to swim a length of a pool."

Words failed me, and I turned away to watch the divers.

I did not like to hear of such talent going to waste. In real life, as well as in fiction, I like stories to have a happy ending.

The spectators applauded as a diver climbed out of the pool. Automatically I joined them, although I can't say I noticed the dive.

I watched the next competitor take off his dressing gown. He was a young, good-looking, blonde haired youth. I counted the steps of the ladder as he climbed – 47 steps. That was some height. I could feel the beads of perspiration standing out on my forehead for him.

The diver moved to the edge of the high board. The crowds held their breath, and I could hear the board creak slightly under his weight. He stood erect, with his toes overhanging the edge of the board. He licked his lips, raised his arms, gracefully straightened his legs and leapt into space.

I counted his somersaults, one . . . two . . . three . . . They were slow and graceful. I could almost hear his body turn in the air; then slowly he straightened out and dived vertically into the water, straight as a spear.

The crowd cheered and applauded. Jeff's eyes sparkled.

"Local boy," he said with pride.

Absentmindedly I glanced at my programme. The young diver was down as W. G. Waters.

"W. G. Waters?" I said. "Is . . . is that Splash Waters?"

Jeff beamed. "The same. That boy's got guts."

"Wow!" I nodded. I felt I was shaking with excitement. "You can say that again!"

BUTCHER, BAKER, CANDLE-STICK MAKER......

Did you know that Alfred Hitchcock, the famous film director, began his star-spangled career as an assistant layout man in the advertising department of a London store? His wage was fifteen shillings a week. This led to a job at a film studio where they made silent films, and soon he was on his way to becoming one of the greatest film directors of all time.

George Peppard, the film actor and star of that exciting film *The Blue Max*, had a variety of jobs before he became a leading movie actor. He was a stone-mason, builder, fencing instructor and a janitor.

You may think that a clerk's job is mundane. In many cases it is but, depending on your personality, you can make it interesting, even amusing. Take the case of Harry Secombe, now a popular star of television and films—remember him as Mr. Bumble in the film *Oliver*? Before he went into the

Des O'Connor wanted to become a writer but instead he became a Butlin redcoat.

Mike Yarwood was sacked when the boss caught him impersonating the customers.

Ken Dodd sold his own brand of disinfectant in the new estates of Liverpool.

Many famous people started their career in an ordinary job

Army, Harry was a clerk at a steel works in Swansea. Every Friday he had to take the wage packets round to the burly steelworkers. But one week Harry got all the pay packets mixed up, and a hard-working steelman found himself with just a few shillings while a tea boy had several pounds.

Of course, you wouldn't keep any job long if you acted in this way more than once, but you never know what a job may lead to in time. H. E. Bates, the best-selling author who wrote *The Jacaranda Tree* and *The Purple Plain*, was a clerk in a warehouse. He started his working career as a junior reporter on a country newspaper but gave it up. Then, in his leisure time away from his office desk, he continued to write.

His stories were about the ordinary people in the villages and small towns he had known all his life. But eventually, it was these stories that led him

to fame and fortune.

Singer Matt Monro used to be a bus driver, except that his name then was Terry Parsons. And Vince Hill, the singer who comes from Coventry, was a pastrycook when he left school. Even today, some fifteen years later, he is still an excellent cook and often helps his wife in the kitchen.

Another Coventry-born star, comedian Reg Dixon, had a great variety of jobs before he became famous in the late forties. He was apprenticed to a watchmaker, worked in a number of car factories and then became a barber's assistant. He lost this job, however, when he dropped a mug through a washbasin!

On the female side, dozens of waitresses have become famous stars. Cilla Black worked in an office, as did Susan Maughan. And that famous comedienne Hylda Baker left the stage

for a while to learn a trade in a clothing factory, but soon returned to the job she really loved!

Success Stories All!
Most comedians began life doing something different to making people laugh. Stan Stennett used to be a lorry driver and Mike and Bernie Winters had a very good business touring the markets until comedy lured them to success.

Ken Dodd, now one of Britain's most successful comics, had his own tinker's business during the day and played working men's clubs in the evening.

He used to take pots and pans round the new estates of Liverpool and he recalls: "My customers used to ask me for disinfectant, as that on the market was a bit too expensive for them. I got to work and perfected my

Hylda Baker and her pet Chihuahua, Cha Cha. She once worked in a clothing factory.

own calling it Kaydee. It went very well and I've often thought of re-introducing it!"

Des O'Connor was keen on writing at school. He came from Stepney in the East End of London and, as his parents didn't have much money, he went into the first job he could find, working at a printers. He thought that would involve writing, but instead he carried deliveries around on a bicycle! Later, in Northampton, he became a clerk in a shoe factory and after National Service in the RAF became a Butlin redcoat. His training in this job led him to becoming a comedian and a top-of-the-bill recording star.

Freddie Davies, Mr. Parrotface, also started his career at Butlin's after spending some time working in an undertaker's!

Sir William Butlin himself began life in a very modest way. He was a drummer boy in the Canadian Army, then a salesman in a Toronto store. But Billy had more ambition than a department store could offer him and he took over a darts stall at Toronto Fair. He came to England and started a hoop-la stall. It was such a success that three years after landing at Liverpool he had twelve men working for him. His one dream was to build a holiday camp and in 1935 he began building his Skegness holiday camp—the first of a series of camps that were to make him a millionaire!

Any job can lead to great success. Benny Hill used to be a milkman, now he's a top comedy star of TV and films; Harry Worth was a miner near his native Bradford, and Johnny Morris, television's jack-of-all-trades, was a farm manager in Wiltshire before he began his world-wide travels. Al Read, another famous comedian, was a big success in business long before he

ever came into show business.

One TV personality who seems to have had the biggest variety of jobs is Simon Dee. Before he hit the jackpot as a disc jockey he was an assistant photographer, a clerk in a ticket agency, a car cleaner, dressing-gown designer, pneumatic drill worker and a vacuum cleaner salesman. Not bad for a man who started life under his real name of Carl Henty-Dodd!

Mike Yarwood, the young impressionist who is rarely ever himself, worked in a Manchester gown manufacturer's warehouse, but he got the sack when the boss caught him impersonating the customers. Likewise, Geraldo, the bandleader and impressario, worked in a London drapery warehouse for thirty shillings a week before launching out into the world of music! Bandleader Edmundo Ros was studying to be a lawyer before he took to music and achieved world fame in the field of Latin American music.

Donald Peers, a top-of-the-bill singer for many years, was intended to be a schoolmaster. He shattered that illusion at the age of sixteen by running away from his home in South Wales and joining a gang of journeymen painters. He travelled the country with them for a year and then, in search of wider horizons, he went to sea as a messroom steward. But this wasn't the life he wanted and he was soon back, working as a painter. It was while he was working in Lowestoft that he joined a concert party as a ukelele player at three pounds a week!

Who knows, maybe all these famous people would have done well had they stayed in one of the jobs that didn't bring them fame. But it all goes to show that if you set your sights high enough, you can get there in the end!

D ick Nelson crouched near the mud wall of the wretched village and listened to the various sounds that drifted through the night air. Two underfed and probably ill-treated curs were howling mournfully; a woman sang a whining song in the local Vietnamese dialect; some men argued in their sing-song voices from a nearby mud house.

Dick moved the M–16 automatic rifle from one hand to another and crept a few more yards along the wall. He was not wearing uniform. He was an Australian and this was Viet Cong territory, about a hundred miles from Saigon, and if the little yellow men found him he would be shot dead.

"Well, I can't hug this wall all night," he muttered. "I've got to get in there somehow. You're on your own, Dick, my boy – a strictly private party. You're breaking all the rules, and if your sergeant knew you were here he'd go mad!"

Somewhere in the miserable village there was a prison – probably mud and reeds – and the villagers had thrown Will Lawson inside it and he'd been there for a week. Quite likely he had been beaten and underfed. It seemed the Viet Cong sympathisers were waiting for some of the Viet Cong regular army to show up.

Apart from his rifle, Dick had an automatic pistol stuck in the waistband of his shapeless peasant clothes. He moved along the wall until he came to an opening. This was it. He had to get inside the village.

He was trained to move with all possible caution. He slipped noiselessly towards the nearest house, and then hugged the wall. The typical smells of the village came to him; someone was cooking and the odour wasn't pleasant!

A minute later he saw two Vietnamese walk out of the cookhouse carrying a small dish of steaming food. They walked to a central mud building. One man, who was carrying a rifle, opened the door and let the other go inside.

"That's the place!" decided Dick Nelson.

Obviously the door was locked and the man with the rifle had the key. Now if he could only get that key! Or

DEADLY TERRITORY

by Norman Lazenby

A grim story of the bitter battlefield that is Vietnam

would it be better to make a silent attack on the two men?

Dick decided to attack. Like a panther coming out of the jungle, he ran swiftly, crouching, every sense alert for danger. He reached the open door, slowed. Flat against the mud wall, his rifle ready, he began to sidle inside the place.

An exclamation in Vietnamese hit his ears and then a lithe, shadowy body swung a rifle butt at him.

Dick Nelson was as fast as the villager – and was better trained. He countered the swinging butt in a split second with his M–16 and then whipped the rifle butt at the head of the little yellow man.

It connected and the Vietnamese sympathiser sank with a groan.

He heard the scuffling sound and just glimpsed the vague outline of the other man in the gloomy hut. Dick threw himself forward, collided with the villager and then used the gun butt so swiftly the man did not have a chance.

"Two out!" gritted Dick. "That gives me a few minutes!"

A choking cry from a dark corner of the stinking place told him where to look. In another second he was bending over his friend, Will Lawson. The young Australian soldier was bound but not gagged.

"You!" gasped Will. "Of all the crazy –"

"We're getting out of here!" chuckled Dick. His sharp army-issue knife began to slice through the manila rope.

"How'd you know I was here?" rasped the other.

"Little spy came to H.Q. You know the type – information is all they have to sell. I gave him money and food."

"I was a fool," said Will. His dry throat almost choked him. "I blundered into those Viet Cong sympathisers . . . shouldn't have been out that night . . . Why didn't the big shots send a patrol out to get me out of here?"

"They're too busy searching for snipers. I knew that and decided to get you out myself," declared Dick. "Now let's go! We've only got a few minutes. I've got a jeep hidden outside this village."

"I've got news for you, pal," said Will in a queer voice.

"What's that?"

"I've got a broken leg. I can't stand. They were slapping me around with bamboo sticks when one little gink got too enthusiastic and broke my leg!"

Dick Nelson gave a low whistle. "Right. I'll carry you. First – a splint."

It was typical of his fast thinking and quick actions that he had the rifle used by the Vietnamese villager bound to Will's leg as a splint in no time. He used his own shapeless cotton jacket to make bandages, tearing it into strips.

"That's a good rifle strapped to your leg, buddy," he grinned. "It's a prize. The North Vietnamese Army uses them – it's a Czechoslovakian SK–47."

He thought he would make sure the villagers were really incapable of making trouble. He tied their hands and legs with the last strips from his cotton jacket.

"Now, for Pete's sake, let's get out of here!" he exclaimed, and he hoisted Will Lawson on to his shoulder.

Dick heard the cry of pain that his friend tried to bite back and he became grim and wary as he stepped close to the outside door of the hut.

If he was seen, his chances of escape with Will Lawson would die the death, because the villagers would have weapons. Guns of all types were plentiful, sometimes stolen from South Vietnamese Forces or found near casualties beside a field of battle.

Dick Nelson watched two older villagers scuttle across the square to some reed and mud hut. Now, he thought, it was now or never. The two Vietnamese in the hovel behind him might start yelling when they recovered their wits.

Will Lawson was a good twelve stone, but that did not worry Dick. He started forward, running for the nearest cover. He paused in the dark shadows. He heard Will moan. His broken leg must be really hurting. Dick ran on again, his rubber-soled boots making hardly any noise. All at once a slant-eyed Vietnamese in drab yellow cotton appeared before him. The man seemed to have darted out from nowhere.

For a fantastically brief moment the native stared, and then he whipped out a knife and crouched before Dick Nelson. Apparently this was his only weapon.

Dick could not use his M–16. The noise would have wakened the entire village.

With Will Lawson on his back it was hard to fight another man. A bit of karate might be usefully deployed here, and instinctively Dick knew which trick to play.

His booted foot kicked out with the speed of a steel spring. It was really fast – and it had to be! The boot thudded right into the villager's middle. He gave a gasp and folded.

He might have recovered quickly enough, but Dick rammed into him with superior weight. Dick's bunched fist chopped down on the side of the

man's head and he went out like an extinguished light.

"I've got to get going!" gritted Dick, and he ran on again.

He turned the outer wall of the village and took big strides into the jungle. He clung grimly to his automatic rifle. Soon the black twining growth of the forest hid him.

Dick Nelson thought everything was going fine and the next thing would be to cook up explanations to his sergeant. That might take some doing!

He had memorised the narrow track through this area of rotting bamboo and ant-hills, and he was sure he was right on target for the jeep.

He ran, gasping a bit because of his

heavy burden, and the outline of the jeep loomed up in the dark. Without pausing, he began to tear aside the few leafy branches he had used as a part camouflage. Will lay weightily on his back. Another second and he would deposit him safely inside the jeep.

It was that second that nearly brought Dick's unauthorised mission to disaster.

He did not hear the Vietnamese – did not even sense his presence, as some soldiers swore they could do!

The native hurled at him. A club was in his hand.

Dick's first awareness was of that heavy club slashing down out of the dark and his grim alarm as he tried desperately to avoid it.

The club hit him on the side of his head as he rolled a fraction of an inch. A pain-racked darkness rushed into his brain. He sank to his knees and Will Lawson slid to the ground.

Dick knew no more. He was lost in a dark land and he could not think or move.

The lithe young Vietnamese stared at the two Australians for a second. Dick was unconscious and Will Lawson had temporarily lost his senses, as agony from his broken leg sliced into his brain.

The Viet Cong sympathiser picked up Dick Nelson's M–16 and appeared to gloat over it. He then found Dick's revolver. He gave a little cackle of satisfaction, glanced again at the two prone men and then raced off into the night.

His intention, apparently, was to summon his friends from the village.

He had taken Dick's two guns, but he failed to consider the North Vietnamese Army issue rifle – the SK–47 – which was strapped like a splint to Will Lawson's broken leg.

For nearly two minutes neither men moved, and only the strange bamboo jungle sighed around them.

Then Will Lawson swam into some sort of sense. He glanced around, remembering the lithe assailant who had been lurking near the jeep.

He tried to waken Dick Nelson, but he was still unconscious.

Will stared desperately at the jeep, realising he could not stand let alone try to drive. He shook his pal once again. Dick Nelson was really out solid!

The next thing Will realised was that the M–16 that Dick carried was gone.

He did not doubt that the native would be back with some of his friends from the Viet Cong village. There was only one thing to do.

As for Dick Nelson, his first recollections were chaotic. His brain began to work, accompanied by some awful shooting pains in his head. Then he forced his mind to clear. He saw the jeep, the jungle and the dark night.

Then came the deadly chatter of an automatic rifle. He whipped around. The familiar noise was right beside him.

He saw Will Lawson throwing shots into the leafy walls of the narrow track leading back to the village. A howl of pain screeched out of the night. The rifle spoke again. Another native yelled and sobbed. Then came the sound of sandals desperately running down the track.

"Hey, let's get out of here!" yelled Dick.

Will grinned up. "You awake?"

"You bet!"

Dick grabbed his pal and gently deposited him in the jeep's passenger seat. Then he got behind the wheel and started the big petrol engine. As it roared into life, he turned curiously to Will.

"Say, that's not my M–16 you're using!"

"That little Viet Cong gook took your rifle," retorted Will.

Dick nodded and slapped his waistband. "He took my revolver, too. So – "

"So I had to use the Czech SK–47," retorted Will. "It's a good thing you used it for a splint. Better than a bit of old bamboo. Hey – let's get going!"

The jeep leaped forward. They were on their way back to base.

coats of many colours

"Beware . . . . . Redcoats!"
Not a cry you would hear nowadays but until comparatively recent times it was commonly heard on the battlefields of the world. The scarlet coats of the British Army may now be used only on ceremonial occasions, but the history of the gay uniforms once worn by the army is still fascinating.

The New Infantryman
The end of the 18th century, the era of the industrial revolution, was a time of change for Britain. Even that stickler for tradition, the Army, underwent its own form of transformation.

In 1797 the coats of all ranks were ordered to be fastened down to the waist, hiding the waistcoats. Lapels were abolished and regimental distinctions shown by buttons and laces. The large cocked hat was replaced in 1800 by a round lacquered cap, later changed to felt, which became known affectionately as the "stove pipe". About eight inches high, it had the regiment's number and a trophy of arms on a brass plate. The cockade had the regiment's button in the centre.

The Duke of Wellington wished for a hat that could not be mistaken for the enemy's in battle, and a new cap designed in 1811 had a higher front with a tuft and cockade on the left, and a plume on the right. It was actually a copy of a Portuguese design. Because of transport and manufacturing difficulties it is doubtful if the hats were worn in the Peninsular Wars at the beginning of the nineteenth century, but fresh drafts from England may have been issued with them. Regiments stationed in Canada during the War of 1812 with America would certainly have been wearing the old style shako.

The alterations in their equipment did not disconcert the British. They received a severe mauling in some actions of this futile war but in others they gave a good account of themselves. At Chrystler's farm, a small clearing in the forest crossed by gullies and deep in mud, the 49th and 89th Foot Battalion, with the aid of the Canadians, defeated an American force

Some infantry caps worn between 1800–15

The 5th and 6th Rifle Battalions of the 60th Foot

rifle, with a 2 foot 6 inch barrel upon which could be fastened a sword bayonet.

Highland Regiments

The Highland Regiments have always maintained a reputation for splendid dress. During the Napoleonic Wars the belted plaid and sporran were worn only by officers in full dress. The ranks wore a small piece of tartan attached to the left shoulder on the same occasions, but on service all these items were discarded.

The grenadiers wore white hackles in their bonnets and the light company green ones. Up to the Corunna Campaign of the Peninsula War, officers wore the kilt while on service, but after that grey or white pantaloons and Hessian boots or trousers and gaiters were worn. In the New Orleans Campaign of 1814–15 the 93rd Highlanders wore the bonnet without feathers.

Highland Regiments wearing the traditional kilt and bonnet, with a be-trewed soldier as comparison.

four times their number who came at them in charge after charge.

Rifle Companies

The West Indies were in ferment. The slaves were in revolt and battalions of troops sent out from England became reduced through casualties and fever and the survivors were drafted into the 60th Royal Americans—a purely British regiment. The 5th and 6th battalions of this regiment became the first rifle units, with the dubious privilege of wearing moustaches. The 5th wore a green jacket piped down the front in red, and red collar, cuffs and turn-backs. The 6th also had a green jacket but their collar, cuffs and turn-backs were in green. Light blue pantaloons were worn by the 5th. Both battalions wore the stove pipe hat with green tufts and bugle horn badges, their equipment being black leather.

95th Rifles

The American Corps proved so effective that a British Rifle Corps was established and several regiments were each ordered to supply a captain, lieutenant and ensign, two sergeants, one corporal and thirty privates. It was to be commanded by Colonel Coote Manningham.

They did not look a typical infantry regiment. They resembled more a cavalry unit, and one officer remarked that they were really "dismounted cavalry". Their arms were the Baker

The first British Rifle Corps, the 95th Rifles

Regimental Bands

An important part of the regiment was the band. Besides playing in ceremonials and leading the regiment on the march, bands were often present in battle.

The musicians and drummers were normally placed in the centre of the square, a form of defensive fighting particularly favoured by the British. On many occasions they were actually in the midst of the fighting. At the battle of Talavera the 48th Regiment were hard pressed to resist the French. The bandsmen put down their instruments and, picking up weapons, joined in the fight.

The uniforms of bandsmen were no less distinctive than those of the soldiers, and indeed would often surpass them for elegance.

The Volunteers

When war broke out with France after the French Revolution, Britain as usual, was unprepared. The army was in chaos, and recruits hurriedly drafted in were often sub-standard.

The country was in real danger, through subversive actions by the French, of sinking into anarchy. Wisely the Government authorised the raising of Volunteer Corps for the defence of the country in the face of invasion or civil strife.

At first some companies were armed only with pikes. Many companies were small but some, like the Royal East Indian Volunteers, could form three regiments complete with bands and Negro musicians.

Two Volunteer Companies raised at the time of the French Revolution: the Royal Westminster and the Bank of England

A Drum Major of the Foot Guards and a Negro drummer

Scottish Volunteers

The Scottish Volunteers generally had the same uniform as the English. One of the most important was the Royal Edinburgh, raised in 1794 and first called the Edinburgh Volunteers. Their uniform underwent many changes later in their career.

The Royal Edinburgh Volunteers, one of the most important in Scotland

The Royal Highland Emigrants, a Canadian regiment composed of Scotsmen

Overseas Regiments

When Canada was ceded to Britain in the 1760s the previous French organisation of the militia remained in force, supported by the influential classes. The American Revolution saw American columns marching to capture Quebec, but the staunch defence of the Empire troops put paid to this hope. Among the defenders was a detachment of Highlanders, the Royal Highland Emigrants, recruited in Nova Scotia, Prince Edward Island and Newfoundland. In 1779 it was numbered the 84th.

At the outbreak of the War of 1812 the fiery cross was sent through the settlements of the Highlanders, most of whom were old soldiers from previous regiments. The cross was the idea of Father Alexander Macdonnell and the stalwarts he gathered were called the Glengarry Light Infantry Fencibles.

Their uniform, like so many other Canadian Regiments, was dark green. The regiment had a distinguished career and took part in many engagements of the War of 1812 before being disbanded in 1816.

Raised by a padre, the Glengarry Light Infantry Fencibles achieved great distinction in the War of 1812

Names & Nicknames

Many famous people have been given nicknames, either in affection or disgust, such as 'Butcher' Cumberland or the more popular 'Winnie' by which Sir Winston Churchill was known to thousands of his admirers. Do you know . . .

1. Who was Old Mooney?
2. Which Australian bird is dubbed the laughing jackass?
3. Who wrote under the name of Boz?
4. Who was the Swan of Avon?
5. Which animal is called the ship of the desert?
6. Who was the Swedish Nightingale?
7. Who was the Scarlet Pimpernel?
8. Who was the Wisest Fool in Christendom?
9. Who was the Young Pretender?
10. Who was the Grand Old Man?
11. Who was known as Longshanks?
12. Who was known as the Iron Duke?
13. Who was the Cock of the North?
14. Who was the Iron Chancellor?
15. Who was Buffalo Bill?
16. What is 'Old Glory?'
17. Which seaside birds are known as Mother Carey's chickens?
18. Who was the Scourge of God?
19. To whose army did the soldiers called Ironsides belong?
20. Which city has the nickname Old Reekie?

ANSWERS

1. Captain Robert Falcon Scott. 2. Kookaburra. 3. Charles Dickens. 4. William Shakespeare. 5. Camel. 6. Jenny Lind. 7. Sir Percy Blakeney. 8. James I. 9. Charles Edward Stuart—Bonnie Prince Charlie. 10. William Ewart Gladstone. 11. Edward I. 12. Duke of Wellington. 13. George, 5th Duke of Gordon who founded Gordon Highlanders. 14. Prince Bismarck. 15. William Cody. 16. National Flag of U.S.A. 17. Stormy Petrels. 18. Attila the Hun. 19. Oliver Cromwell's Army. 20. Edinburgh.

GAS FROM THE SEA

Turn on a tap, light the gas and immediately you have a warm, steady flame. Nothing could be simpler, could it? We may take it for granted, but in fact that gas might well have come from the cold depths of the North Sea, brought to you after the expenditure of millions of pounds on research and equipment.

But let us start at the beginning, going back to the time when the sea was free of the strange shapes of the drilling platforms searching for the gas pockets.

After the discovery of one of the world's largest gas-fields in north-eastern Holland a few years ago, geologists became interested in what might lie under the bed of the North Sea. The rocks there are similar to those found in both Britain and Holland, rocks which could hold large pockets of gas and oil, trapped by an impervious layer known as 'cap-rock'. Geologists reasoned that what existed on land could just as easily be found under the sea.

EXPLORATION

In 1962 exploration began. Surveying ships and planes swarmed over the North Sea for three summers, collecting valuable geographical information. Results showed that conditions were favourable for finding gas, but the only way to get positive proof was to drill.

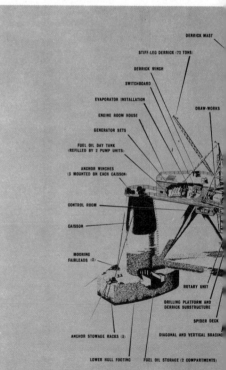

British Petroleum's floating drilling platform Sea Quest *being towed to the North Sea. Figures on the platform illustrate its size.*

A cut-away diagram of Sea Quest. *Built at a cost of £3½ million, she can accommodate sixty men and weighs approximately 7,700 tons.*

By 1964 the British Government had invited applications for licences to search for gas and oil in the North Sea. The area allocated to Britain by international agreement was divided into blocks of 100 square miles and companies were awarded the right to search in certain blocks. British Petroleum, which has over thirty of these blocks, started work on their first well the following year.

SUCCESS—AND DISASTER

Their first drilling platform, *Sea Gem*, capable of raising itself on its own legs, planted them firmly on the sea bed and sent down an exploratory drill. Over three months later its efforts were rewarded when the hole showed traces of gas; and this on its first attempt. But it was not enough to be of value commercially.

Drilling continued and then British Petroleum announced that Britain had struck it rich, and the gas was very high quality too. It was 94 per cent methane with little nitrogen.

But, lucky though the *Sea Gem* was, its luck finally ran out. As it was being prepared to move to a new site it capsized and sank, taking down many of the crew. The tragedy delayed production of the gas, but two more platforms were built near the site of the sinking and soon their drills were biting into the sea bed.

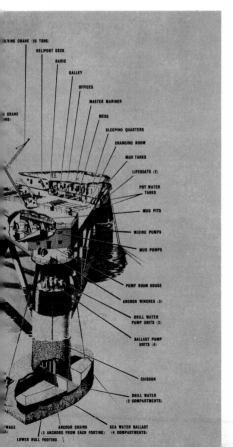

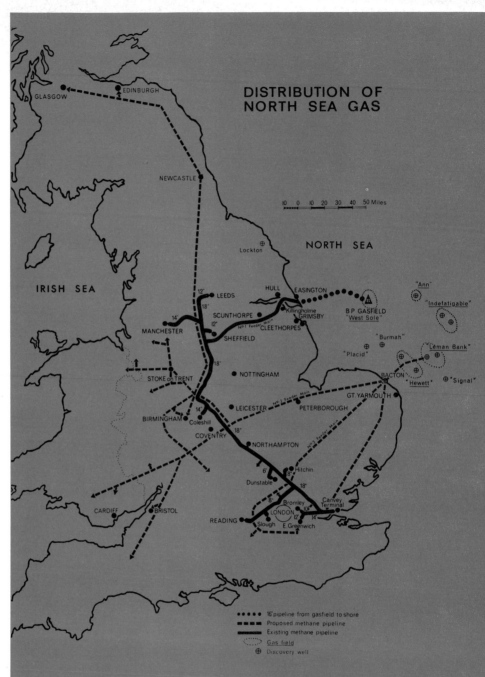

North Sea gas is fed into the methane pipeline and reaches many large cities. New pipelines proposed will reach over most of Britain.

A FLOATING RIG

Drilling platforms which rest on the sea bed are practicable in the southern part of the North Sea, where it is generally never more than 150 feet deep, but depths of over 300 feet are common in the north. A drilling platform which would float and be able to drill in any depth of water was therefore ordered by British Petroleum from the Belfast firm of Harland and Wolff

and this, named the *Sea Quest*, was launched in 1966.

The *Sea Quest* is one of the largest off-shore drilling rigs ever built. It is a tripod design, each side over 100 yards long, standing on three huge legs, legs which give it an overall height of 320 feet. When on tow to sites these legs are normally 23 feet under the water, but by flooding them with nearly 13,000 tons of sea water she can sink to a drilling position where her pontoons will be 80 feet beneath the surface. In this position she can drill a hole 20,000 feet deep if need be, held steady by nine anchors weighing 30,000 lb. each. Quite a piece of equipment, altogether.

LIFE AT SEA

What of the men who work aboard this floating giant and others like her?

The work, of course, is hard. But the crews generally have excellent sleeping quarters, recreational facilities and good food. And no rough sea crossing for them. Instead they are flown out by helicopter, dropped off on the special landing pads on the platforms, do their stint aboard and are then taken off by helicopter again without ever setting foot in a boat.

GAS PIPELINE

Locating the gas in the first place is hard enough but then comes the mammoth task of getting it to the mainland. British Petroleum have agreed to supply 100 million cubic feet of gas per day, and with a flow like that nothing must go wrong.

Work on the pipeline for bringing the gas ashore began almost as soon as the *Sea Quest* was on site. Approximately 13,000 tons of 16-inch-diameter pipe was delivered to British Petroleum's main operational base at Great Yarmouth and then the 40-foot lengths were tar coated, covered in concrete for protection and welded together. A special barge laid out the pipeline on the sea bed and another followed behind, using high-pressure jets to scoop out a trench to bury it. The North Sea is treacherous at the best of times. Foul weather, large glacial boulders on the bottom and sometimes the odd wartime mine were just some of the hazards to be overcome during this operation.

March 1967 was a historic month in the story of North Sea gas. In that month the first natural gas from British Petroleum's West Sole field came ashore in East Yorkshire. The flow was kept low at first in order to clear the 45-mile pipeline of water, a plastic sphere in front of the gas scouring the water out as it was pushed along. The gas was afterwards refined and distributed into the methane grid. The diagram shows the full extent of this grid.

By spring of 1968 most of the essential work on the West Sole field had been completed. Several wells had been drilled from the two fixed plat-

A fixed-leg drilling platform.

forms and equipment to remotely control them was installed, so both men and drilling rigs could be removed from the platforms.

So the next time you light the gas, possibly North Sea gas, just spare a thought for all the work that has gone into making that pot of tea.

BEHIND THE SCENES

by A. Booth

Roger took no side in the conflict between the Houses of York and Lancaster, but he would help any creature in distress.

The little Yorkshire town of Ring-caster was all agog with excitement, though it was only sunrise.

For on that Corpus Christi Day, the Thursday after Whitsun 1463, the great event of the year was to take place: the performance of a cycle of Mystery plays by the workmen's Guilds.

The inhabitants paid no heed to the struggle going on not far away between the two rival Houses of York and Lancaster, which some called the Wars of the Roses. For that was a fight between the great barons for power which fortunately did not affect ordinary folk, who went about their business as usual, not caring if the White or the Red Rose triumphed.

Young Roger Firth had come to see the acting from the balcony of the largest inn, owned by the father of his friend Tom.

The crowds were already massing at certain spots where the great movable stages or 'pageants' were to stop, each with its own Bible play.

"Here is a programme of the scenes," said Tom. "There are eight, and each is acted by a different trade Guild."

Roger took it and read:

"Mercers. The Fall of Satan.

"Cobblers. Adam and Eve.

"Carpenters and Shipwrights. Noah and the Ark.

"Fleshers. The sacrifice of Isaac.

"Barbers. David and Jonathan.

"Shepherds. The Nativity.

"Chandlers. The Crucifixion.

"Tanners. The Day of Judgment."

"This is the starting-point," said Tom. "Then they move on to the Market Cross and so to all the other stations, and the second play will come here, and so on, so that everyone sees a different scene at once."

"I'm glad we're here," said Roger. "This balcony is a rare place for seeing."

"The highest bidder among the citizens has the right to choose the spot," said Tom. "It cost my father a pretty penny to have it here."

"I expect he gets it back in custom," laughed Roger. "How long will the whole cycle take?"

"All day long, though there is a short interval between the arrival of the different pageants. It's a very short one, and it's my job to run ahead when the scene is finished and give warning to the next station."

"I wish we hadn't such a long wait before it begins."

"Would you like to go behind the scenes and see the actors? I'm helping with the dresses and properties."

So Roger followed his friend to the house hired by the merchants to store the properties and the great two-decker six-wheeled wagons from one year to another.

Here all was excitement and confusion, as the players dressed for their parts.

The lower stage of the wagon, besides being used as a quick-changing room, represented Hell, and some of the prentices were dressed as demons in red, blue or black, with hideous masks over their faces, while the Devil himself pranced about in his rough hair coat, for he was always a comic character.

The upper storey of the wagon was the stage proper, and a ladder led up from it to 'Heaven'.

Roger stood watching the angels having their skins painted gold and their wings fixed on with wire. The Saints all had gilt hair and beards. The wicked characters wore black coats and the good ones white, so that everyone knew whom to hiss or cheer.

The chief tanner of the town, wearing a long beard and dressed in a white cope and gloves, was carefully fixing his crown in front of a shining steel mirror.

"That is God Almighty," said Tom, "and there is the Serpent." He pointed to where one of the

mercers was struggling into a one-piece garment of coat, hose and tail.

"Come and help me check over these articles, Tom." cried a man dressed as a bishop and supposed to be the High Priest. "Try and find the hook for Judas to hang himself with."

Tom hunted about and discovered it under a pile of Noah's ark animals.

"Has anyone seen David's sling?" said one of the barbers.

"And the toys for the shepherds' presents to the Child—a rattle, a ball and some cherries?" cried another.

"They sell Judas's hook and David's sling by auction after the show," said Tom.

Roger found himself pressed into service. He painted over a hole in the hose of the Archangel Gabriel, and was then asked by a fierce demon to lace up his coat, which fastened at the back.

"Where is my Herod's coat?" cried a half-dressed member of the Fleshers' Guild. Find it for me, Roger, lad."

But the boy could not see it anywhere.

"It might be in one of the cupboards in the next chamber," suggested Tom. "Through that door."

So Roger passed through into a small room, where a number of empty chests and wardrobes showed where the costumes had been kept.

Only one cupboard was shut, and

when he went to open it, though it had no lock or bolt or fastening, he met with some resistance.

Exerting all his strength, he gave a mighty pull and the door flew open. And he saw a number of costumes inside.

He put his hand in to take out the Herod coat, and felt something moving, something soft and warm.

He drew back his hand sharply, thinking that some animal was inside that might attack him in panic.

But it was no animal, but a woman, who stepped out to confront him.

She wore the clothes of a lady of fashion, though they were stained and muddy; her hair was dressed carefully, and her shoes were of fine

leather, though scratched and mired. Her hands were white and smooth and her bearing gracious and commanding.

They stared at each other for a few seconds and then she said: "So you have found me. What will you do with me?"

"What are you doing here?" he stammered. "No women take part in the Mystery plays."

"I was hiding," she answered, "from my enemies."

"Your enemies? Who are they? I am sure you are not fleeing from justice."

"You are right," she replied. "Tell me if you are for York or Lancaster."

"I do not know," he said.

"Not know!" she exclaimed. "Are you for Henry VI, your lawful king, or for the usurper who has seized his throne, base Edward of York? Do you favour the Red or the White Rose?"

"Lady, most of us take no sides in

Ringcaster. We only wish to be left in peace. Let these quarrelsome barons settle their disputes without our help, they will destroy themselves in time. There is nothing to choose between them. They only seek power and riches for themselves. We do not care whom we call King."

She looked at him with scorn and shrugged her shoulders.

"So be it," she said. "But you will not give me up to my enemies?"

"That I will not, though I do not know who are your enemies or why they seek to harm you."

"They are the Yorkists. They have crushed us for the moment, but we shall raise another army. I was on my way to Scotland, but I was taken by a troop of bandits. I managed to escape and fled here last night. Seeing this house closed, with no sign of life about it, I entered by a broken window. But a crowd came in this morning and I hid in the wardrobe."

"You can go whenever you like.

Nobody will stop you. They are all busy dressing for the Mystery play."

"I cannot. I have heard coming from the next room a voice which I know. It is the voice of one of my greatest enemies–Sir Edward Moulton. Though you say the townspeople are not interested in the war, Sir Edward is a bitter Yorkist."

"He owns much land near here," said Roger. "Today he has come to the plays. No doubt he is talking to the actors."

"If he finds me here he will seize me or kill me," she said. "Can you lend me a disguise?"

"Wait a few minutes," said the boy. "I must take this coat to one of the players, or he will come seeking for it here."

Hurriedly he returned to Herod and gave him the costume.

Tom met him with the news that one of the demons had sent word that he was ill and could not come.

"It does not matter," Tom said. "There will just be five demons instead of six. But will you please take his costume and put it away in one of the cupboards in the other room, so that it will not get messed or tumbled?"

When Roger got back to the lady he said: "Put on this suit and the mask and go in and mix with the players. If anyone troubles to count

the demons, you can pretend that though you are sick, you made the effort and came after all."

"But I do not know the part," said the lady, beginning to unfasten her dress.

"You need not act at all. The scene is the very last one—the Day of Judgement. It will not be seen until tonight. There is no need for anyone to be dressed so early, but the Master of the Mystery insists on it. But, as any of the players can slip out and watch the other scenes, covered with a cloak, you should be able to leave whenever you wish. Sir Edward will be on the balcony of the inn and it will be safe for you to go."

"Oh, you are a noble boy!" she exclaimed. "Especially as you do not feel pledged to either side."

"I would do the same, lady, for any creature in distress," he said gravely. "My father says that neither side seeks the good of the country, but only its own selfish ends."

When she was dressed he looked through the door and said: "There is a great crowd in there. Let us go among them."

As they entered the room, she faltered and shrunk back, but Roger pulled her forward towards Tom.

"He was able to come after all," he said.

"That is good," said Tom.

"But he still does not feel very well and would like just to sit still and be quiet," said Roger.

"Do as you please, man," said Tom grandly, full of importance, and he rushed away on some other errand.

"Now I must go back to the inn," said Roger to the lady. "When you leave here where will you go?"

"To a cottage five miles from here where I can seek shelter with an old serving-woman of mine. I was on my way there yesterday when I was captured, but after my escape I found the way blocked."

"And will it not still be?"

"I must take that chance, and it is a better one now that I am disguised. Do you think this odd garment will draw too much attention?"

"Not today, for plenty of the players will be wandering round till their turn comes. You can remove the mask when you are out of the

city and tie your head in this kerchief."

He picked one up that was lying on the floor. "And you'd better have my cloak to cover you. The effect will be that of a man at first glance, now that those long skirts are gone."

Tom, who was passing, saw him holding the cloak out and said kindly: "Poor fellow, he feels cold with the sickness. See, boy, you'd better go home and not try to act, or come in later on."

"He'll go later," said Roger, "after the weakness has passed a little."

"Let him rest in the other room, out of this crowd," said Tom.

So, assisted by Roger, the lady made her way out of the crowded dressing-place and settled down on a pile of sacks.

"I will bid you farewell now," said the boy, and he kissed the hand she held out.

"God be with you," she replied, "and help you to see where your true allegiance lies. I shall never forget your goodness, and if my cause should triumph, I will find means to reward you."

He opened the door and passed through the other room, more crowded than ever.

"Look you, master," said one of the demons to an angel. "When you throw me into Hell, be a little gentler. I have a bruise on my leg the size of a groat from the last rehearsal."

"Try and make more smoke for that scene," said the master of the tanners to his stage-manager. "And be sure the gates of Hell open and shut properly. There was not enough noise coming out last time."

"Will this do?" asked the other, and set a string of pans clanging.

"Now, boy, we are ready," said the mercer. "Run and tell them at the inn."

So both boys went back to the *Green Dragon*.

All day long the wagons lumbered up to the inn, the players acting their scene, and then moving on to the next station, to be followed by another pageant.

The audience sat entranced as the great Bible stories were pictured before them. Most could not read, and this was one way in which the truths of religion reached them. Every incident was as real to them as one in their own lives.

In the middle of the barbers' play of David and Jonathan a slight disturbance caused Roger to look around. He saw a rough-looking man beckon to Sir Edward Moulton.

The knight left his seat and walked with the man along a balcony to an inner room.

Roger slipped after them and crouched down under the window. It was on the side of the inn away from the road and all around was deserted.

"I tell you I had her safe," the visitor was saying. "We were disguised as a band of robbers, and I put her safely under lock and key. But she managed to escape."

"Where did she go?" said Sir Edward impatiently. "North, towards Scotland, I suppose?"

"No, that was impossible. I had guards thickly posted in that direction. She must be here somewhere, for she was seen outside the town gates last night before they were closed.

"Have you questioned the guards at the gates?"

"I did, but nobody like her had passed them. They would have remembered a high-born lady with no cloak and with torn and dirty clothes."

"Then she must still be in the town. I will have every house searched."

"You will have to wait till the end of the plays. You cannot enter private houses while the citizens are out."

"Curse the plays!" cried the angry knight. "Let us make other plans, then. She cannot leave without going . . ."

Roger did not wait to hear any more, but ran as quickly as possible to the pageant house.

It was empty and he heaved a sigh of relief. The players in the last scene were away in another part of the town now and would soon be arriving at the inn.

"She must be safe now," he said. "In that disguise she can have passed the gates easily."

His mind relieved, he went back to the balcony to see the last scenes.

It was dark and torches had been lit as the tanners' pageant lumbered to a stop before the inn.

The lost souls were thrown into Hell, which was a great dragon's mouth gaping wide to receive them, and throwing out real smoke and flames. The Blessed had ascended into Heaven up the rickety ladder, and the Mystery plays were over for another year.

He walked with Tom back to the pageant house to help in storing away the costumes and properties.

As he was staggering into the inner room with an armful of clothes, he noticed a packet lying on the table.

It had been made from one of the programmes of the cycle, folded round something hard. A piece of lead lying beside it had written his name on the outside.

Inside was a gold piece and a torn scrap of the parchment on which was inscribed:

"From your Queen, Margaret of Anjou, wife of His Majesty, King Henry VI, of the House of Lancaster."

ODD FACTS

NOBODY REALLY KNOWS WHAT CAUSED THE TOWER OF PISA TO 'LEAN'
IT WASN'T SUPPOSED TO LEAN WHEN IT WAS BUILT; IT WAS SUPPOSED TO STAND STRAIGHT.
IT WAS INTENDED AS A BELL-TOWER FOR THE CATHEDRAL NEARBY AND WAS STARTED IN 1174 AND FINISHED IN 1350

THE HUMMING BIRD DOESN'T REALLY FLY LIKE OTHER BIRDS. ITS WINGS BEAT AT THE RATE OF ABOUT FIFTY-FIVE STROKES A SECOND! THIS REMARKABLE WINGPOWER WAS DEVELOPED BECAUSE OF THE BIRD'S EATING HABITS. IT FEEDS ON THE NECTAR OF FLOWERS AND ON THE INSECTS IN THE FLOWERS. WHEN POISED OVER A FLOWER THIS BIRD SEEMS ABSOLUTELY STILL IN THE AIR; THIS IS BECAUSE ITS TINY WINGS MOVE SO FAST. IT THEREFORE AVOIDS TOUCHING THE DELICATE FLOWERS, WHICH WOULD BE UNABLE TO SUPPORT THE BIRD'S WEIGHT.

THOMAS BABINGTON MACAULAY (1800-1859) BRITISH STATESMAN, HISTORIAN & ESSAYIST, HAD A PHENOMENAL MEMORY. FROM THE AGE OF THREE HE HARDLY EVER SEEMED TO STOP READING, AND EVERY-THING HE READ HE REMEMBERED. HE COULD TAKE IN THE CONTENTS OF A PRINTED PAGE AT A GLANCE.

ALTHOUGH THE MAIZE PLANT MIGHT NOT LOOK MUCH LIKE A FACTORY, IT IS A SUGAR FACTORY. IT WORKS EVERY DAY FROM DAYLIGHT TO DARK. FOR IT TO MAKE SUGAR, JUST TWO THINGS ARE NECESSARY: CARBON DIOXIDE FROM THE AIR AND WATER FROM THE GROUND

A SPANISH TRUMPETER IS OLD SLANG FOR AN ASS; THE PUN BEHIND THE NAME WAS "DON KEY"

EUROPEAN FRESHWATER EELS PERFORM ASTONISHING MIGRATIONS. FOR YEARS THE EELS LIVE IN INLAND POOLS AND PONDS, THEN SUDDENLY THEY BEGIN LONG AND HAZARDOUS JOURNEYS, IN VAST NUMBERS, TO THE SARGASSO SEA IN THE WESTERN ATLANTIC. THIS JOURNEY CAN TAKE 2½ YEARS

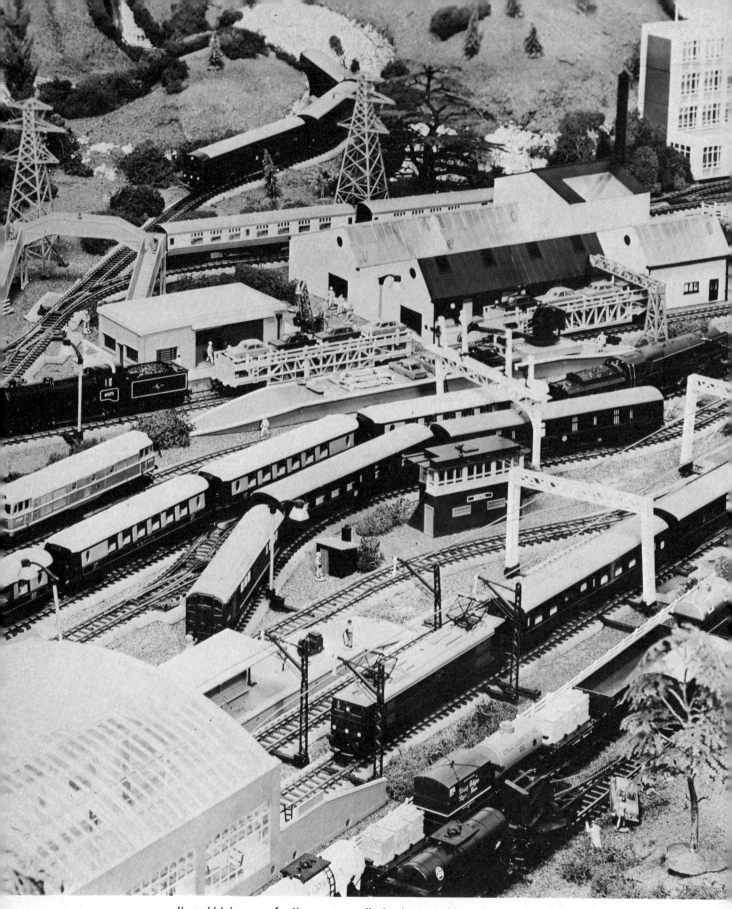

It could take years for the average collector to assemble such a spectacular layout, complete with model village and trackside scenery.

Miniature Masterpieces

Peter Flanagan takes an exciting trip . . . on a model railway.

The electric locomotive glides slowly into the station and picks up a train of freight wagons. The signal is against it, but soon it is allowed to pull out, passing on the way the Royal Mail on its journey north. Over bridges, through cuttings, rattling across points, the train picks up speed. But an obstacle is seen on the line ahead —a matchstick. The operator slows down and flicks the match aside.

Perhaps you've guessed already. It's just one of the many hazards encountered in running your own model railway.

Enthusiasts in this country number hundreds of thousands and they're not all young boys. Fathers and sons, and sometimes mothers too, join in this fascinating hobby.

Most large towns have clubs for the model railway enthusiast. Junior sections exist for the younger members, who can usually find within the clubs everything they may need for their hobby. Their libraries are crammed with books on the subject and their own circuits are open to the youngster.

But the real enthusiast, to whom the hobby is a way of life, does more than just run trains around track and read books. Trips to railway museums are organised, outings to loco sheds and other places of interest where the devoted gaze in awe. All this and more make the world of the model railway addict a fascinating one.

Many enthusiasts like to make their own models, but the majority prefer to buy them ready-made. Perhaps the biggest model railway manufacturer in this country is Rovex Scale Models of Margate, Kent, who make the famous Triang/Hornby models, known to collectors around the world and exported to almost every country. The marvellous details of the models are perhaps taken for granted by the collector, but a tremendous amount of research and design goes into their production.

Choosing the Model

When Rovex decide to bring out a new line the various departments go into a huddle and thrash out the many possibilities. Should it be one of the famous steam engines or a sleek diesel? Perhaps it is time to bring out one of the crack American monsters?

At a meeting of department heads the final selection is made. It must extend the range, yet be different from the rest. If possible it must be able to use parts already in stock. If a chassis already in production for other models can be used then so much the better, because the chassis is an expensive item and the collector could put different bodies on the same chassis. Spares and replacements would be easier to obtain. Above all, the new model must be what the public wants.

Once a decision has been made, the appropriate plans are obtained from British Railways. Not only is the model to be remarkably accurate, it will be a miniature of the real thing. Photographs are also used to check the appearance.

A prototype is then made. Called a rough, it is made by a skilled engineer who may take a month over it, creating all but the most fussy detail. Items which would only break off the moment the model was used are deliberately not shown.

Checking the Prototype

If an entirely new chassis is required it is cut out of a solid piece of metal. The body is made up from plastic. Experience has shown that it is best to start off with materials which will be used when the final product goes into the shops.

The model is now passed back to be approved and if it is suitable it goes into the Drawing Office, together with the original works plans and photographs. Working drawings of the new model are made, checked, and sent back to the Development Department.

A proving model is now constructed from the firm's own drawings to show that they are correct. Absolute precision is essential and it may take as much as 1,000 man hours to complete —a normal weekly stint for one man of five months. When it is ready, the proving model is tested on track and some go to the Development Department for further testing.

Processes and Patterns

The first stage in making any model is forming the mould. First, a master copy of the mould is made from sheet plastic or wood. From this, using a panto-graph, the first metal mould is made, a process which could take months. Each may cost over £1,000 per locomotive mould, and nearly as much for a coach.

The mould is taken to the moulding machine. Here it is placed in position and a special powder poured into the machine which, when heated and pressed, forms the plastic body of the mould. The stores issue up to 10–12 tons of this powder every week, yet each body weighs only three ounces.

Close to this another important process is taking place. A huge ribbon of steel is being fed into a machine, and out of the other end emerges coupling bars, hooks and rods. Five coupling bars can be made every second.

Track is made in two parts—the plastic base is moulded by a similar process to that of the locomotive bodies, and rails are cut from whole reels. Every week some 200,000 pieces of track are made.

Such is the demand for model trains that at any one time the factory may have up to 850 different mouldings in stock and nearly 2,000 components in the stores. And every process, from conception of the idea to tightening the final screw, is carried out in the one factory.

Made to Scale

Three basic scales are used on model railways. The 00 scale means that 4 millimetres on the model is equivalent to 1 foot on the real thing, say a loco-motive. HO denotes a scale of 3½ millimetres to the foot. The old TT scale has now been replaced by the new 'N' of 1:160.

True scale reproduction can be applied to models but in the case of the ordinary layout equipment, such as a station, it is virtually impossible. The average railway station can accommodate up to ten coaches on its platform and this would mean constructing a model station eight feet long.

Showing scale on a curved piece of track is another problem. The minimum line radius on British Railways is 792 feet, which would be 9 feet on 00 gauge. A complete circle of track would be 18 feet across. In actual fact the curved sections are made to a radius of 17

An exotic form of rolling stock. When a spring is released the sides fall away and two rockets swing out ready for firing.

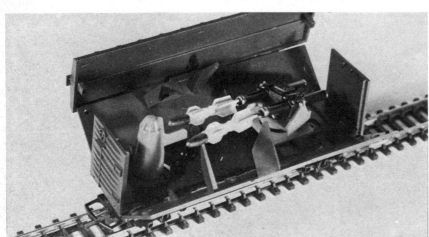

inches, giving a complete circle of only 3 feet.

Maintaining your Equipment

A model train is simple in design with little to go wrong. But to make sure that it stays in good running order it is essential that all parts are kept clean.

The power controller must be in good condition or, of course, the locomotive just won't go. The electrical connections are held to the box by a knurled nut holding down a brass tag on the end of a wire. The nut may work loose, allowing dirt to become trapped between the connection. If this happens it is easily remedied by turning the power off—a simple precaution usually forgotten—removing the nut altogether and cleaning the connection with a clean cloth or fine emery paper. Take one wire off at a time so you won't forget where each goes.

Upkeep of the track is really important. Care must be shown when cleaning it or it could be damaged. Never use a rough abrasive such as sandpaper or emery as this could allow the track to rust, and always wipe it with a clean cloth. If your track is dirty then it follows that the wheels of the rolling stock will be dirty too, so don't forget to check.

Ensure that all fishplates are in position and not showing rust. This could impede the flow of current around the track and slow down the train. Any fluff between the rails should be picked out with a pair of fine tweezers.

Going in for Repairs

The wheels on most locomotives pick up the current from the track, and therefore they must be checked regularly if your models are to stay in

A true reproduction of the famous Flying Scotsman.

Dinner is now served. A model Pullman train shoots out of a tunnel at high speed.

Model trains, authentic in every detail, rattle through a station, creating an extremely life-like scene.

perfect condition. A handy way of cleaning them is to turn the locomotive over, and touch one plug of the rail connection onto the eyelet which secures the metal strips making contact with the back of the wheels. Place another connection onto the metal chassis. Turn on the power and the wheels should spin round, and a fine abrasive applied to the edges will scour off excess dirt.

Fluff and dirt often accumulate inside the motor of the locomotive. To get at this vital piece of equipment remove the screw securing the body— this should be easily seen as there is only one screw which fulfils this purpose— and lift off the plastic body. Most dirt will be found around the commutator, caused by the normal wear of the carbon brushes. Press on top of the brushes against the wire spring and the brushes will lift away from the commutator. Push a small rag into the commutator and clean it by turning the armature by hand. While doing

this you could perhaps check that the brushes are not worn.

If they need replacing, the wire spring at the top can be unclipped and the brushes lifted out. Note which way the tag with the wire on it, taking current to one of the brushes, is fitted.

Finally, a few drops of oil on the pads at the front and back of the motor and some on all moving parts, such as wheel axles, and your locomotive should be in perfect condition.

Happy railway modelling!

BE a SCRAP MODELLER

Murray Collier shows you how to save money on your model railway accessories by making them yourself.

Any model railway would look bare and unreal without buildings and other accessories on it, but it can be expensive to buy ready-made models and kits. The answer is, of course, to build them yourself and this can be much easier and cheaper than most boys realize. By using scrap materials, many of which have some resemblance to the finished model, many items can be made that have a far more realistic appearance than shop-bought models.

Every model maker, no matter what his interest, should keep a scrap box. This should be divided into as many

A general view of part of a layout which includes an electric roadway. Authenticity is added by the partly-built house—top centre—and the use of pine cones as ornamental trees; these give an excellent effect when painted.

compartments as possible. No old materials should be thrown away, they should go into an appropriate compartment in the scrap box. In this way a modeller can quite often put his hand on just the piece of odd material he needs.

Old electrical equipment should be stripped right down to its component parts; it is amazing what useful pieces there are in, for example, an electric plug—nuts, bolts, fibre washers, pieces of plastic, strips of brass or copper, and so on. Sort the parts into the different sections of your scrap box.

Your father may often have a broken tool which he was going to throw away; this is another good source of supply for the model-maker. Mount the broken piece of tool on a good handle, using a strong glue. The tips of old files are good for modelling, as are hacksaw blades, small chisels and the like. The main thing is to have the tool small enough to work on your delicate models.

Nests of small drawers are very useful for items like nuts and bolts, and these can be made easily and quickly from matchboxes. Collect as many as you can and glue four or five side-by-side to form a base, and then as many layers as you like on top of them. You can give the whole thing a good finish by pasting a strip of old wallpaper, or something similar, round the bottom, sides and top, which will strengthen it. A small bead can be glued or sewn to the front of each tray to act as a handle, or trays can be pushed out from the back when required, which is much simpler.

Boxes of matches cost very little so you can build a nest of twelve drawers for a small sum, and still have all the matches left—just don't leave them lying around loose.

Now for actual modelling in scrap materials. Practically any material can be used, the main consideration being whether it is the right scale, and what sort of fixings can be used on it. Adhesives will be the main method of joining but you will find that polythene is practically impossible to glue without special adhesives. All other materials are fairly simple to deal with.

Making a Polythene Model
The first model I shall describe is made partly of polythene but no adhesive is used. This is a simple water storage tank which will fit very well on any layout of 00/H0 scale.

You will need a small-size plastic bottle used for washing-up liquid, four

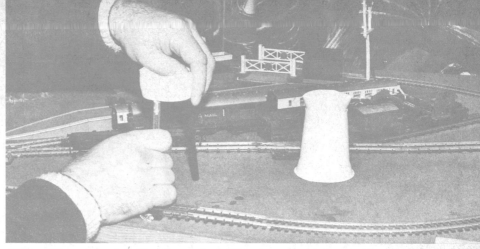

Fitting the pen "legs" to the storage tank. The pens can be of any colour as long as they are the same shape. On the right is a cooling tower waiting to be filled with plaster.

old plastic ball-point pens, four screws or nails that will fit tightly into the tops of the pens, and a piece of thick cardboard larger than the base of the bottle.

Carefully cut off the bottle about 1½ inches from the base; the bottom will be the storage tank. Scrub it hard to remove as much of the wording as possible, so that it will not show through the finishing paint. Smooth any rough edges with glasspaper.

The most difficult part of this simple model is the next stage—and even that isn't very hard! The piece of cardboard must be cut to an *exact* square a little bigger than the base of the bottle, and then diagonal lines drawn from corner to corner, so that the centre of the card is found. Draw a circle the same size as the bottle base, using the crossing mark as the pivot for a compass, and then another circle half an inch inside the first. Cut away the cardboard *outside* the outer circle and *inside* the inner one. Make four holes in this ring where the crossing lines still show on it. They should be just big enough for the pens to fit tightly when pushed through.

Lay the cardboard ring on the bottom of the storage tank and mark the position of the holes by pushing pins through the centres. Now take the pens and cut off the tips, leaving the remainder about 4 inches long. Rub off the brand name with a file or glasspaper. The model is now ready for assembly.

Push the nails or screws through the base of the storage tank from the *inside* and then fit the pens over the points and push them home. You may need to screw the screws down tightly. Slip the cardboard ring on to the pen legs and adjust it about halfway up. Your model is now complete and ready for painting, but more about this later. A ladder made of wire can be hooked on, if desired. This model is best fitted in one place on a layout, or a piece of cardboard can be used as a base and nails or screws pushed up through it into the ends of the storage tank legs.

Now try another!
Another simple model can be made very easily from plastic yoghurt pots or cream cartons. They must be of the

Fitting up a netting fence on a model railway. The wire will stop the net from stretching too far and will keep the posts the correct distance apart.

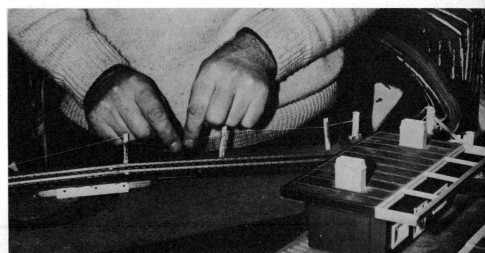

Plastic ends can be bought from any good model shop and mounted, like this, on a hardboard frame which is then covered with balls of wallpaper and strips of cloth soaked in thick wallpaper paste. Paint the exterior thickly with a brown or grey paint and, while still wet, sprinkle with coloured sawdust. The "girder" bridge on the right is made from a piece of plastic curtain rail.

type that taper towards the top. Because of the size of the pots, this model, a factory cooling tower, is best suited to 00 or N gauge. All that is needed is two pots and some plaster of Paris, Polyfilla or something similar.

Cut off the top of one pot about half an inch from the rim and the other pot about 1½ inches from the rim. You will be using the *base* of the first pot and the *rim* of the second. Mix up some plaster to a thick cream and pour it into the pot until it reaches the rim, then turn the cut-off rim of the second pot upside down and push it down into the plaster. Settle it firmly until the two pots are touching all round, wipe off any plaster that has oozed out, and finally pour in some more plaster at the top, to within a quarter of an inch of the rim.

You now have a tower which is broad at the base, narrow or 'waisted' about three-quarters of the way up, and slightly wider at the top. The model should be painted concrete grey and the inside of the top a sooty black. And there is another scrap model complete.

Everyday modelling materials

Another handy modelling material is the plastic 'netting' used for pre-packed vegetables. This comes in at least two sizes of mesh but it is the very smallest that is of use to modellers.

Cut it into strips about three-quarters of an inch wide and it is ideal for fencing, tennis court nets and so on. The only problem is fixing it to posts, because it is one of those plastics which ordinary adhesives will not fix. One of the simplest ways of fixing it is to trap it between the two halves of a fence post.

The posts should be about half an inch longer than the width of the net—1¼ inches long—which will allow for a quarter of an inch to be sunk into the baseboard and a quarter of an inch to project above the fence. Split a post down the centre and spread glue on the two inside surfaces. Place one end of the netting on the glued side of one piece and then lay the other piece back on top. Bind the *bottom* of the post firmly with thread.

For binding the top of the post you will need either thread or heavy gauge fuse wire in long lengths. Bind the top of the post as before and then weave the long end of the thread or wire in and out of the net mesh for about three inches, just like the supporting wire on a real fence. At three-inch intervals put further posts and treat in the same way. The thread will hold the fence to shape, because the netting is extremely elastic and can stretch to double its length.

Make sufficient holes in the baseboard for the fence posts and glue them into position. When the glue has

set, run another thread or wire along the bottom of the fence in the same way as the top one and the fence will be held quite firmly.

One of the handiest scrap materials for modelling is ice lolly sticks. These are made of strong, smooth wood, thin enough to be shaped easily and light enough for quite delicate modelling. Collect as many as you can for your scrap box—not, of course, off the ground, but whenever you or your friends have ice lollies. Wash and dry the sticks and you will find them useful for dozens of ideas in model making. They are already miniature planks but they can be cut down for fences, walls, roofing, coal bins in railway yards and so on.

After being held in the steam of a kettle with tongs or tweezers for a while, they can be bent to various curves, or they can be placed in a dish and boiling water poured over them. When shaping with this method, the sticks must either be fastened into the shape desired while still damp, or be pinned to the model immediately and allowed to dry into shape.

Painting your models

Some tips on painting, or more precisely, colouring, can be very helpful, because more models are spoiled by bad painting than by anything else.

The first thing to remember is to use the right colouring for the job. Only special paints should be used on plastic, otherwise not only will the finish look all wrong, but the paint will not last and will soon begin to peel off and leave the model looking most dilapidated.

There is a range of paints developed specially for plastic models. These are called "Humbrol" and your local toy or hobby shop will probably stock them. You will find that the range includes such useful textures as grass, concrete, asphalt, and so on. Use a concrete finish for your water storage tank and cooling tower, working the paint well into the cardboard ring of the tank as this will stiffen the cardboard and also hold it in place on the pen legs.

For the plaster at the top of the cooling tower a different colouring must be used. Wherever possible avoid using paint on plaster because it tends to look artificial. It is better to use some kind of stain. It is often possible to mix powdered colouring with a plaster before water is added and the simplest way of getting the sooty black appearance to the top of the cooling tower is to mix soot with the plaster while it is still dry. If you use plaster for earth or rocks, or other natural effects, never use a paint.

Stains can often be made at home: strong cold tea, fruit juices, ink, creosote, iodine and many other things you will find in the house can be used and can be mixed for different shades.

When your models are finished— whether scrap models or shop bought —it always pays to make them look that much more realistic by 'untidying' them a little. The trouble with most models is that they look just too good to be true. Try running a smokey candle round the top of the cooling tower while the paint is still wet. Take care that the smoke and not the flame touches the paint. This will give a grimy effect, as though smoke had swirled over the rim of the tower. One or two windows should always be opened in a building, even if it means cutting out the frame and remaking it. Old property should have one or two broken windows, either by carefully breaking the plastic or glass or by drawing black cracks on the inside of the glass. Dirty some of your layouts to get a more natural effect: railways never stay clean and tidy for long, even when they are new.

Save yourself money, have better looking models and a lot more fun from them by making use of those old thrown-out materials: be a scrap modeller.

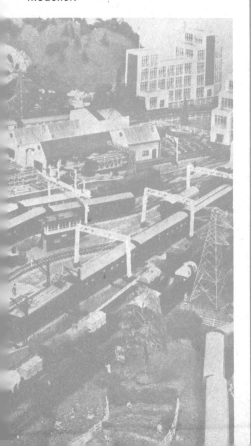

tinker, tailor... and author.

Many famous writers followed other jobs or professions before turning to authorship. Can you name any of the following? . . .

1. The clergyman who wrote about Tom's adventures with the Water Babies.

2. The Hudson Bay Company's clerk who wrote about life in the South Seas.

3. The young barrister who wrote about Rudolph Rassendyll's adventures in Ruritania.

4. The river boat pilot who took his pen-name from a familiar call used on the river.

5. The newspaper reporter who wrote about the Four Just Men.

6. The 'Tinker of Bedford' who wrote about the Celestial City.

7. The doctor who created the character of Sherlock Holmes.

8. The solicitor's clerk who wrote about the Five Towns.

9. The London magistrate of the eighteenth century who wrote about Tom Jones, Jonathan Wild and Amelia.

10. The sailor who wrote about the fortunes of the Beverley children.

11. The draper who created the first British space story.

12. The Post Office clerk who wrote novels about Barsetshire.

13. The bootblacking boy who created the character of Mr Pickwick.

14. The famous diarist who first worked as a tailor's assistant.

15. The cashier from Ireland who became a famous playwright.

16. The country schoolmaster who became England's most famous dramatist.

17. The volunteer cavalryman who wrote the Waverley novels.

18. The engineer who wrote *Treasure Island*.

19. The market gardener who wrote about the Doones.

20. The railroad policeman and miner who wrote about Tarzan of the Apes.

ANSWERS

1. Charles Kingsley, 2. R. M. Ballantyne, 3. Anthony Hope, 4. Samuel Langhorne Clemens—Twain (Mark), 5. Edgar Wallace, 6. John Bunyan, 7. Sir Arthur Conan Doyle, 8. Arnold Bennett, 9. Henry Fielding, 10. Captain F. Marryat, 11. H. G. Wells, 12. Anthony Trollope, 13. Charles Dickens, 14. Samuel Pepys, 15. George Bernard Shaw, 16. William Shakespeare, 17. Sir Walter Scott, 18. Robert Louis Stevenson, 19. R. D. Blackmore, 20. Edgar Rice Burroughs.

THE FABULOUS TABLET

by Phillip Barratt

For long, weary years I had pursued this tablet, as ancient as time itself!

They wonder why I come here every day to the Museum to stare at the Rosetta Stone. They think me mad because I sometimes talk to myself, because my emotions get the better of me . . .

Cursed stone! To think that I once held your elusive Inca counterpart within my grasp! Fame, riches and renown would have been mine for the asking. For long, weary years I pursued this tablet, as ancient as time itself. The key to all the wisdom of

the past! What knowledge! What pageants of lost history revealed!

Through trackless jungles, over mountains, through pestilential, disease-ridden swamps, across vast, aching, arid stretches of desert; up dangerous jungle rivers with death lurking behind every tree trunk, pursued by death in a hundred different forms—head-hunters, wild animals, disease, snakes, fever. Tortured by loneliness and fear, day in, day out. Pestered by thirst, hunger, heat, flies; or aching, shaking with fever in some damp, dripping, poisonous jungle, and all because of a stone!

I curse the day I ever took up archaeology! I curse it for stealing my youth, my health, my sanity. You and your counterpart, with its cursed secret. Now, it will never be known. It lies buried deep in a festering South American jungle . . .

I was sick when they brought the news of its whereabouts. Ravaged with fever in a vermin-infested hotel in Chimborazo. Somewhere deep in the interior, beyond the source of the Rio Tigre, a tribe of Jivario Indians had come across some ancient ruins. Inca ruins, perhaps. The stone was there . . .

Fear had gripped me then. Supposing it should be gone before I regained sufficient strength to undertake the arduous journey through many hundreds of miles of unexplored jungle! Supposing others should get there before me!

Again and again I raged and struggled to get out of my sick bed, only to fall back, weak and exhausted, almost mad with the fear of losing it after all those years of heart-breaking toil and pursuit.

There was only one thing for it. Sunac, my native guide, would have to go ahead, find the stone and guard it until I was well enough to travel.

That I should want him to beat through hundreds of miles of jungle to guard a stone struck him as another sign of the white man's madness.

"But, senor," he argued, "there are many old stones here in Chimborazo!"

"You will leave at once," I told him. "Do you know where to find the ruins?"

"I know the ancient place you speak of," he said, "but the way is dangerous. The Indians are those that treasure human heads, and mine, senor, would suit me better on my shoulders . . ."

The promise of trade goods persuaded him in the end and he set off, still convinced that I was insane.

The weeks crawled by, and I was filled with a fury of impatience to get away. Still weak and far from well, I started off into the interior, ill-equipped and without sufficient porters, my money having long since run out.

The going was not too bad and I managed to keep up a fairly good pace in spite of my weakness.

But as we progressed deeper into the leprous jungle, my troubles started. Deep mud and swamp began to clog our progress. I can still hear the sickening, plopping sounds our feet made in the slimy mess underfoot.

But even more foul than the mud was the loathsome presence of Luigi Mannessi. He appeared, seemingly

out of the ground, one evening, looking like some monstrous toad with his bulbous features and bulging stomach. He was accompanied by two villainous half-castes, armed to the teeth. They eyed my stores and equipment with avaricious eyes.

I had heard a great deal about Mr. Mannessi. Rumour had it that he had originally escaped from Devil's Island, killing two guards in the process. Since then he had roamed the jungle, robbing and murdering to his heart's content, secure in the knowledge that no member of the

"I think you do," he said, his hand dropping to his gun holster.

It would have been madness to argue under the circumstances. But I was determined to have the last say in the matter. Mr. Mannessi might know the jungle like the back of his filthy hand, but he knew nothing of the root I slipped into his stew later that evening.

Soon all three of the murderous villains were snoring like pigs. We quickly broke camp and slipped off into the night; but in our haste to escape we lost most of our stores while fording the river.

I almost cried with vexation as I watched the precious trade goods and invaluable medical stores being carried away by the rushing torrent.

Step by step I grew weaker and weaker. The porters, heavily laden as they were, found it difficult to adjust their long, swift catlike lope to my stumbling crawl. Nor did they attempt to conceal their contempt. Of what use was the white man's magic now, they mocked.

Long before we reached the Inca ruins they deserted, taking most of what was left of the stores with them. A small handful stayed with me, dazzled and hypnotised by the picture of miles of gaily coloured cloth and innumerable shiny hatchets, which I promised them as a reward for their services.

I was beginning to entertain hopes of reaching the encampment before our stores ran out completely when a tribe of Puyo headhunters waylayed us. They picked off three of my remaining Indians with their deadly blowguns before I even knew what was happening.

They brought us before their head man, and I'd hardly opened my mouth to speak when they all crowded round me, poking their filthy fingers into my mouth.

It was my gold teeth—they had never seen anything like them. This was indeed magic of a special kind!

"A mouthful of sunshine!" they cried.

I suffered their mauling and probing with a pretence of smiling and good humour, and was rewarded by their allowing us to go free.

They even went so far as to reple-

law would be fool enough to venture into the green kingdom of Hell.

He greeted me with all the friendliness of a python about to enjoy a leisurely meal.

What was I doing so deep in the heart of the jungle? he enquired, solicitously. Did I not know that it was dangerous to deviate from the beaten track?

"This is not my first trip into the interior," I answered shortly.

"No doubt you are seeking gold?" he smiled, displaying a mouthful of rotting teeth in the process.

"I am not interested in precious metals," I replied. "I am an archaeologist. There are some ancient Inca ruins hidden somewhere in the jungle, and it is my intention to find them."

"These Incas decorated their idols with gold and precious gems, did they not?" he put to me slyly.

"Not always," I retorted, turning my back on him.

"I think I will help you find these ruins," he smiled oilily. "I know this jungle like the back of my hand."

"I'm sure you do, but it so happens that I do not need your help."

nish our sadly depleted larder. A brief trip into the jungle with their blowguns and they came back laden with wild pigeons and game.

And so we pushed on, through the steaming undergrowth. Tearing, cutting and fighting our way through the clinging, enveloping, choking mass. Tortured by the sticky heat, mud and mosquitoes by day, and shaken by fever by night, I was reduced to a mere skeleton. But I reached the encampment . . .

Sunac was there to greet me. My weary bones cried out for rest, but first I had to see the stone.

"Where is it?" I cried impatiently, "take me to the tablet!"

"But you are sick," he objected. "The stone has waited a long time, it can wait a little longer. Look, I have prepared you a place to lie down. Tomorrow, or the next day, perhaps. . . . ."

"Not tomorrow or the next day," I groaned, "but now. Lead me to the stone at once!"

"As you wish," he shrugged, leading me through the ruins.

Another time I should have been thrilled by the antiquity that surrounded me, but now I had no eyes for anything but the tablet.

"Here it is," cried Sunac proudly, leading me to a white, shiny slab. "It was very dirty, but I managed to chip it clean . . ."

Chip it clean! Indeed he had. Every mark, every word, every hieroglyphic, had been painstakingly chipped off . . .

$ 5000 REWARD
BILLY THE KID
DEAD OR ALIVE

WHEN IN JUNE 1878, DEPUTY SHERIFF MARION TURNER ARRIVED IN PECOS VALLEY TO RESTORE LAW AND ORDER, THE WHOLE REGION WAS UNDER THE CONTROL OF THREE POWERFUL CATTLEMEN AIDED BY HIRED GUNS, MERCENARIES OUTSIDE THE LAW. THE HEAD OF THIS CRUEL BAND WAS NONE OTHER THAN BILLY-THE-KID! THE CLASH BETWEEN THESE TWO MEN HAS BECOME KNOWN IN HISTORY AS:

THE WAR IN LINCOLN COUNTY

PLEASED TO SEE YOU, SHERIFF. I HOPE YOU DON'T FALL LIKE YOUR PREDECESSORS UNDER THE BULLETS OF BILLY-THE-KID.

IF ONLY WE COULD UNITE TO CLEAN UP THE REGION.

GATHER TOGETHER ALL THE CATTLEMEN IN THE SALOON TONIGHT. I HAVE AN IDEA.

OUR NEW SHERIFF DOESN'T SEEM TO HAVE ANY WORRIES.

IS THIS THE MAN WE HAVE BEEN WAITING FOR, FOR SUCH A LONG TIME?

YOU ALL WANT TO WORK IN PEACE AND SECURITY. FIGHT TOGETHER AGAINST THE OUTLAWS TO RESTORE ORDER.

WELL SPOKEN.

LET'S FORM AN ARMED PATROL TO PUT AN END TO THIS REIGN OF TERROR IMPOSED BY THE CHISUMS, MACSWEENS AND OTHER CATTLE KINGS.

AND A FEW DAYS LATER A POSSE OF 35 VOLUNTEERS WAS FORMED.

NOTHING SUSPICIOUS ON THIS SIDE, TURNER!

BILLY AND ABOUT 50 HIRED GUNS, ARMED TO THE TEETH, ARE RIDING IN YOUR DIRECTION.

LET'S GALLOP AS FAR AS THE CANYON... WE HAVE A MEETING WITH AN OLD FRIEND, AND MUST NOT KEEP HIM WAITING!

THE MERCENARIES ARE A FEW MILES AWAY...

THESE PEASANTS WANT TO IMPRESS ME WITH THEIR SISSY OF A CHIEF... THEY WILL REGRET IT!

FIFTEEN MINUTES LATER, IN A NARROW CANYON...

HERE THEY COME!

IT'S AN AMBUSH!

BANG!

POW!

OUR MEN ARE FALLING LIKE FLIES. WE WILL ALL GET KILLED IN THIS HELL HOLE. WHAT SHALL WE DO, BILLY?

BILLY IS GETTING AWAY... FOLLOW HIM!

THAT NIGHT, IN THE NEIGHBOURING HILLS...

PUT OUT THAT FIRE, YOU IDIOTS. DON'T YOU REALISE THEY ARE LOOKING FOR US?

AFTER TWO DAYS OF SKIRMISHES AND OF BEING FOLLOWED, BILLY-THE-KID RETURNED TO LINCOLN

IS MR. CHISUM IN?

DON'T GO IN. HE DOESN'T WANT TO SEE YOU AT ANY PRICE!

AFTER ALL I HAVE DONE FOR THAT SCUM, HE WILL SEE ME WHEN I WANT!

MY DEAR BILLY, I CAN'T GET YOU OUT OF THIS. WOULD YOU LIKE SOME MONEY TO GET YOU INTO MEXICO UNTIL YOU ARE FORGOTTEN ABOUT?

BE SERIOUS, BOSS! WHAT I NEED IS MEN AND AMMUNITION!

DON'T PUSH ME, KID! YOU'VE MADE SO MANY MISTAKES THAT I'VE GOT TO KEEP OUT OF IT!

BUT AT THE MACSWEEN RANCH THE WELCOME IS WARMER...

COME IN, FRIENDS, TURNER WILL NEVER DARE TO LOOK FOR YOU HERE!

BILLY, THE SHERIFF IS COMING THIS WAY... WITH TWO COMPANIES OF THE 9TH CAVALRY!

GOOD GOD, WHAT A NERVE!

DEFENCES WERE PREPARED AT THE MAGNIFICENT RANCH HOUSE...

THAT MATTRESS, OVER THERE...

SOON THE RANCH WAS READY FOR THE SIEGE...

I PROMISE THEM A LOT OF FUN...

SUSAN, PLAY THEM SOME WARLIKE HYMNS!

EXCELLENT IDEA!

THIS TIME, TURNER AND HIS POSSE WERE DETERMINED TO FINISH OFF THE JOB...

WILLIAM H. BONNEY SAYS RUMOURS OF BILLY-THE-KID WERE HEARD FOR THREE MORE YEARS. FINALLY, IN 1881, HE WAS IMPRISONED AND CONDEMNED TO HANG. HE SUCCEEDED AGAIN IN ESCAPING. HOWEVER, THREE MONTHS LATER, SHERIFF PAT GARRETT PUT THE FINAL TOUCH TO THE CAREER OF THIS SINISTER INDIVIDUAL BY SHOOTING HIM DOWN AT FORT SUMNER!

THE END

A ZANZIBAR SLAVER

by Tony Oldfield

How can a handful of disguised British tars hope to overcome the Arabs on the huge slave-trader and free the prisoners?

The three naval officers on the quarterdeck of the top-sail schooner, *H.M.S. Ulysses*, stared at the graceful Arab dhow as it sailed slowly past their anchored warship. On the raised poop of the dhow stood a group of Arabs. One of them shouted across the intervening gap.

Lieutenant Grant, commanding officer of the *Ulysses* called to Abdul, the ship's interpreter: "What is he saying?"

"He say, why you not come for a sail with him one day."

"Insolent devil!" muttered Lieutenant James. "It's sickening to think that we can't arrest these slave traders right here in Zanzibar. If only we could do that we could smash the slave trade."

"True," said Midshipman Richard Marsh, "but if we stop them on the high seas surely we are being almost as effective?"

"If, is the word," grumbled Grant, "you've not been serving in this ship long, but long enough to know we haven't much chance of catching these fast-sailing dhows. And, don't forget, there are only seven ships in this squadron and all the sea between East Africa and Arabia to patrol."

The three men silently watched the dhow move into the harbour and drop anchor. All around lay ships of a dozen nationalities.

The year was 1840 and the Royal Navy was endeavouring to break the slave trade which had existed for centuries. Africans far inland were overwhelmed by raiders, brought down to the east coast of Africa and then endured a two-day voyage to the island of Zanzibar. Here, in the central slave market, they were sold and large numbers were shipped by the fast sailing dhows to the coast of Arabia. Once there they would disappear inland in Asia. Only at sea could the few ships of the Royal Naval slave squadron try to intercept the slave craft and save some of the unfortunate natives.

"The one who spoke, sir," broke in Abdul. "He was Hakkim El Kebir. I have seen him in the slave market. He owns a dozen dhows. He is a great trader."

"We will watch his craft," said Grant. "We are ready for sea. If he slips out, so shall we."

For several days the dhow remained at anchor, but one day, at dawn, a shout from the deck brought Lieutenant Grant hurriedly from his cabin.

Midshipman Marsh said excitedly: "Hakkim's dhow, sir! It's vanished."

"Very well, Mister Marsh. We will get under way immediately. Send a messenger below for Mister James."

There was soon a bustle aboard the *Ulysses* as the crew of some fifty men raced to their various stations. Before long the schooner was moving out of the harbour and rising and falling to the swell of the Indian Ocean.

"Which course do you wish me to follow, sir?" asked Lieutenant James.

"East about the island, if you please, Mister James. My informers ashore have given me rumours of slave concentrations at two bays we have explored before and also a narrow, little known creek."

"Pity we have to wait until they are outside the territorial waters before we can attack," said the midshipman.

"Yes, and once they are outside they can out-manoeuvre us," replied Lieutenant James.

"Oh, don't be so pessimistic," said the commander, "we will catch up with one of them some day."

Some hours passed and the *Ulysses* changed course to enter one of the bays indicated by Lieutenant Grant. The glistening sandy beach was almost deserted. On one section, however, there was a flurry of activity round a small, single-masted dhow.

Lieutenant Grant had his telescope to his eye and declared: "That's too small to be Hakkim's craft. Probably just a fishing craft. But heave to, Mister James. Mister Marsh, take away the longboat with Abdul and find out what they know."

"Back the fore tops'l!" came the cry of the Boatswain.

The schooner soon lay bobbing gently in the bay. The longboat was launched and, with the midshipman in the sternsheets, was pulled rapidly shorewards.

As the men of the *Ulysses* approached, the crew of the dhow—about half a dozen men—stared for a few moments. There followed an urgent discussion. Finally they turned and ran for the protective line of trees which bordered the wide beach. The longboat crunched sand and the sailors sprang ashore.

"Guilty action for peaceful fishermen," said the midshipman to Boatswain's Mate, Cartwright.

"They saw we were armed, sir," replied the sailor. "In these parts, 'when in doubt run for it' is prob'ly their motto."

The seamen, with cutlasses at the ready, approached the dhow and climbed aboard. The top deck was deserted. The midshipman, followed by Cartwright, cautiously lowered himself through a hatchway. The two men found themselves in the hold of the vessel. It extended from bow to stern and was quite empty. There was barely four feet headroom. Attached to both sides were chains and manacles, silent evidence of the usual cargo carried.

"The only fish this craft carries is human fish," declared Cartwright.

"Yes, she's a slaver alright," said Marsh, "although a small one. Probably belongs to some Arab in a small way of business. Not one of the big men like Hakkim."

"What shall we do, sir?" asked the Boatswain's Mate. "Set it on fire?"

"What, in territorial waters?" exclaimed the midshipman. "No, we'll tow it out to the *Ulysses* for a start. I must report to Lieutenant Grant."

The crew of the longboat heaved and pushed at the dhow. With the looms of their oars used as levers, they eventually edged the craft into the sea. Leaving two men in the captured vessel, one to tend the tiller, the other to handle the tow-rope, the longboat was soon being pulled strongly back to the *Ulysses*.

Once alongside the schooner the midshipman clambered aboard and reported to his captain.

"Well," said Lieutenant Grant, after he had heard the story, "as you did not actually attack the dhow, merely discovered it as it were, I think I am justified in seizing it. We will tow it out to sea, set it on fire, and then continue our search for Hakkim."

"May I make a suggestion, sir?" asked the midshipman.

"You may, Mister Midshipman, you may. But I shall probably ignore it."

There was a hint of a smile on the face of the lieutenant and, emboldened by it, Marsh continued: "You have explained to me in the past, sir, that one glimpse of the tops'ls of the *Ulysses* will send slavers racing away."

"True."

"Could we not use the small

captured dhow, sir? I could take an armed party aboard and patrol the coast without recognition. If we came across Hakkim, or any other slaver, I could approach without difficulty. I could either board, or, if you are cruising just out of sight, a signal rocket could bring you down upon us."

"Dangerous," retorted Lieutenant James, "you might all get your throats cut."

"Of course it's dangerous," said Lieutenant Grant, "but I think it is an excellent idea. One of our nine-pounder guns could be shipped in the bows of the dhow. That would give you excellent teeth. If you could dismast a dhow by gunfire the *Ulysses*

would come up and do the rest. But first we must tow this dhow out to sea. We want no prying eyes ashore to witness our activities."

Shouted orders brought the schooner into the wind and, with the long-boat hoisted and secured, the two vessels moved out to sea. When almost out of sight of land, a raft, loaded with empty casks, was set on fire and pushed away from the two vessels. A column of smoke mounted to the sky, marking the apparent end of the captured dhow.

A gun was swung from the *Ulysses* and lashed to the foredeck of the dhow. Twenty sailors, armed with muskets and cutlasses, swarmed aboard and were joined by Boat-

swain's Mate Cartwright and Gunner's Mate Hoskins.

There was a last minute consultation on the quarterdeck of the *Ulysses*, then Lieutenant Grant said: "You have a good crew and I have let you have, in Cartwright and Hoskins, our two most experienced petty officers. Abdul will also be useful if you get close to an Arab craft. But, as I have said, you must try to avoid action beyond attempting a dismasting. Keep to the course we have agreed and, if you have no success, rendezvous here at this hour tomorrow."

"Aye, aye, sir," said the midshipman. He swung himself over the side of the schooner and dropped lightly on

to the deck of the dhow. He called to Boatswain's Mate Cartwright: "Stand by to make sail!"

"Aye, aye, sir!"

Before long the dhow was rocking on the waves, clear of the schooner. Most of the crew were hauling up the huge spar supporting the great lateen sail. With its peak towering aloft it was clearly designed for the special wind conditions of the Indian Ocean.

The dhow's course was set southwards, roughly parallel to the coast, while the *Ulysses* stood out to sea. Within the hour the schooner was hull down on the horizon.

"I want only four men on deck," said Richard Marsh to the Boatswain's Mate, "the rest pack down below. This is supposed to be an innocent fishing vessel, don't forget."

Most of the crew filed below and the midshipman heard one upraised voice saying: "Cor! It's fair like a coffin, ain't it? Fancy bein' cooped up 'ere as a slave for days at a time."

Richard Marsh heard the reply of the Gunner's Mate: "P'raps it'll help you to realise 'ow lucky you are on your comfortable mess deck on the *Ulysses*."

"Hoskins!" called Marsh. "Search below and see if you can find some matting or sacking to throw over your gun. We may have to bear a fairly close inspection."

"Aye, aye, sir!"

The gunner's mate soon reappeared followed by two seamen bearing bundles.

"I've got enough sacking to hide the gun, sir, and I also found, right forward, some of the outlandish clothes these 'eathen Arabs wear. 'Spose those on deck ought to wear them."

"Good man!" said the midshipman. "Abdul, help us to get dressed properly."

It was not long before the men on deck looked like passable copies of Abdul. Richard Marsh then altered course slightly so that he would pass within sight of the second bay which Lieutenant Grant had suspected was used for the loading of slaves. It was empty.

Another hour or two passed and still Richard could see, through his telescope, the faint signs of the *Ulysses* topsail on the horizon. They then approached the mouth of the creek which was also under suspicion. As they passed a headland their first glance was sufficient. At a rough landing stage, half hidden by trees, lay a large, two-masted dhow. Across the intervening water came the babble of voices and the crack of whips. Crowds of people appeared to be in the process of being driven into the vessel.

Marsh could not delay. The crew of a peaceful fishing dhow on a coastal passage would not stop and stare at what was probably such a common sight. He gave no helm order.

Boatswain's Mate Cartwright was horrified. "We're not just goin' to leave 'em, are we, sir?"

"You know the orders. They've got to be out at sea."

Marsh sailed on until they turned the next headland. Then he ordered his vessel to be hove to. What now? How long would the loading continue? In the meantime the *Ulysses* was sailing on, ignorant of Marsh's halt.

The day dragged on. The crew were on edge. The sun beat down and life in the tiny stuffy hold was almost unbearable. The men ate some biscuits, drank some water—and grumbled.

Richard ordered his craft out to

The skill of the Arab manoeuvre was too much for the midshipman. "No good trying to keep away," he shouted to Hoskins. "This tiny boat is no match for Hakkim. Abandon your gun! All hands on deck! Muskets and cutlasses!"

From the hatch poured the British seamen, yelling for battle, their muskets cocked ready for the fray.

Hakkim's dhow was rapidly approaching the captured slaver, the Arabs on board now looking apprehensively at the tough sailors who faced them. Too late they had realised that they were not dealing with only four men.

Richard Marsh moved among his men. "Pick your own targets, and fire when I give the order! We'll show 'em how to fight!"

Then, as the two ships rapidly neared each other, Marsh barked out his order. Twenty muskets fired in unison and there were screams of pain from the Arabs, sitting targets for the crackshot British seamen.

The huge slaver crashed alongside the tiny dhow, and with a loud cheer the sailors swarmed aboard. The Arabs were no mean fighters and were inflamed by the insolence of the disguised attack of the accursed Englishmen.

Bitter hand-to-hand fighting broke out on the already bloody deck of Hakkim's dhow. Men of both sides fell, wounded and killed. The two entangled boats swayed dangerously as Arab and seaman lashed at each other with sword and cutlass.

Richard Marsh fought his way to the poop, where Hakkim had just cut down one of the English sailors from behind.

A desperate struggle between the two leaders ensued, and Marsh finally lunged at the Arab, driving his cutlass through his arm and toppling the huge man overboard.

When they saw their leader beaten, the rest of the Arabs threw down their weapons and huddled, frightened, in the centre of the boat, surrounded by a ring of grim-faced, panting seamen.

Marsh called Abdul to his side and told him to cast a line to the floundering Hakkim. "Tell him he once invited us to sail with him some day, and here we are!"

sea. He did not wish to risk being left behind by the swift two-masted craft when it did emerge.

At last, towards dusk, the lookout gave the alarm. Against the darkening loom of the coast two white sails could be seen. The midshipman ordered a course which would gradually converge upon the slaver's.

Gunner's Mate Hoskins, in his unfamiliar Arab garb, lounged against the matting which hid his precious gun. An able seaman was at the tiller. Richard and Abdul squatted on the deck, amidships. Below, the Boatswain's Mate alerted the remainder of the crew.

The outline of the slaver grew clearer.

Abdul said to Marsh: "It's Hakkim, sah! The big man on the poop!"

Richard could see the deck clearly. There seemed to be about fifteen men sitting or lying about. Hakkim strolled to the side of the poop, stared at the small craft, and then turned away.

"Now, Hoskins, are you ready?"
"Aye, aye, sir!"
"Fire when you bear!"

There was a few moments pause and then the gunner's mate put the glowing match of his linstock to the gun. There was a deafening roar and splinters flew from the slaver's mainmast.

"Got him!" cried Hoskins. "The next one will give 'em something to think about!" Instantly two seamen emerged and reloaded Hoskins' gun. Aboard the slaver there was an uproar. There was a second crash as Hoskins fired again, and the Arabs' consternation increased as the previously damaged mainmast shuddered under the impact of the cannonball and slowly fell overboard.

The Arabs immediately cut away the wreckage of their mast and now, with only the foremast of the dhow effective, the fuming Hakkim shrieked out his orders to alter course and bear down upon the impudent attacker.

JANUARY FOOL

by R. J. Stevens

It took a brave man to dive into the creek on such a bitter night

New Year's Eve. And a bitterly cold one at that.

Old Hank Marney gazed at the long, winding trail ahead of him, frost· reflecting the moonlight, and could not help wishing he was still next to the warm fire he had left behind, at his camp by the Belle Fourche River. However, he had been invited to a party in Deadwood and he was looking forward to it. He was wrapped up well and, though the distance from his camp to Deadwood City was more than twenty miles, he was resolved not to let anything prevent him going there.

Sunshine, his dun gelding, had taken him about ten miles when what he had dreaded took place. It began to snow, heavily. The first snow of the whole winter, and it had to fall now, of all times, he reflected.

"Dang it!" he cried aloud, making Sunshine jump nervously.

Hank never liked snow at any time, and least of all at a time like this —when he was out in it.

Still, he thought, it shouldn't be long before he was inside the warm and cosy Golden Garter Saloon, enjoying the friendly atmosphere along with other prospectors and miners. Almost everyone he knew would be there, having a ball. And if he had as good a time as he had the last New Year, then it was worth the ride in any weather.

Hank was still thinking about the saloon and the party there—gazing at the sombre contour of the Black Hills that drew closer and closer to him—when he suddenly heard the sound that changed his whole night: plus a few of the days that followed. The sound was one which instantly struck terror into him. The sound of someone in great distress. A cry or a scream—it sounded like both. Then all at once he heard a splash in the creek, a small distance away, which led almost parallel with the trail.

In great panic Hank stopped his horse, dismounted and ran towards the creek, slipping and sliding on the frost and freshly fallen snow.

The bank of the creek was high, and upon reaching it he found it hard at first to perceive the water below in the darkness. Then, suddenly, his range-wizened eyes caught sight of air bubbles, rising intermittently, close to the water's edge.

At once he rushed down the bank, half falling in his haste. Reaching the bottom, he swiftly sent a hand groping into the water. But no use, he told himself, he wasn't low enough to feel around properly.

Quickly, he got down to the frosted mud, lay flat on his belly so that he could probe further with his hand. It was at this point, with most of his arm in the water, that he realised how cold the water really was. Ice had already formed in a thin layer, and he knew it wouldn't be long before the creek would be frozen solid.

Not getting anywhere with his hand, he changed round to submerge one of his legs so that he could probe with a foot instead. It was here that he slipped, or rather tumbled forward, awkwardly.

Hank had been duly reluctant all the while to go into the water. He had hoped he could save a life from drowning without putting on himself the agony. And now he was in, he let out a teeth-chattering howl. It was the coldest thing he had ever experienced.

Just as soon as he had got over the shock, nevertheless, he filled his lungs with the freezing air and braved a dive. He spent nearly a minute below surface, feeling all sorts of slimy objects; but, alas, he made no contact with a human body.

After coming up for air he dived a second time, on which occasion he realised his hands were now too numb to feel anything.

Upon surfacing once more, he saw how futile his efforts were. Minutes had elapsed since he had heard the splash, and it was obvious that, whoever the person had been, they would have drowned by now.

Then he heard it, just as he had waded into shallower water by the bankside.

It was the cry he had heard before, but closer and clearer this time. It reminded him of the throaty cough he sometimes gave when his asthma was bad and playing him up . . . Like an agonising gurgle.

Suddenly he saw a sharp ripple on the surface about thirty yards away, saw something dark bobbing up and down for a second or so, then submerge with a splash.

Hank didn't hang around to think how strange it was that the distressed person had somehow moved all that distance away. Instantly, instead, he took a clear dive back into deeper water, then swam for the life of him.

"Hold on, there! I'm comin'!" he shouted.

The swim took a lot out of old Hank, his clothes and heavy sixgun weighing him down, and when he reached the spot he thought was the right one, it took him more than a minute to revive himself in order to make another dive.

He was not properly revived when he did make the dive, however, and his lungs almost burst with the effort. When he surfaced, nothing retrieved, his vision was blurred and he felt his blood pumping hard and irregularly through head and heart. He was all in.

From somewhere around he heard the barking of a dog, heard his horse's whine, then heard a man's voice. Immediately Hank shouted for help as loud as he could, made an effort to wade his way out of the creek. He passed out as he reached the bankside.

After that Hank had vague memories of being carried by someone and lying in a chuckwagon on the move. He recalled someone peering down at him where he was lying, trying to make head or tail out of the words he was mumbling about someone being drowned.

But after that he knew little more until he awoke in a strange bedroom, to find sunlight pouring through a window.

A man entered the room, and Hank recognised him as Alexander Finchley, a rancher whom he often saw when visiting Deadwood.

"Happy New Year," Alex smiled. "It's the first day of January."

That didn't interest Hank. His mind was on one thing only, and that was all he wanted to talk about.

"Did you . . . did you save the other as well? The one who was drowning?" Hank asked seriously.

The rancher kept on smiling. "But there was no one else, Hank. It was you who was nearly drowning. And probably would have if I hadn't passed by the creek at that particular time," he stated.

"But there was someone else," Hank insisted, "that's what I went into the creek for. I saw 'em and I heard 'em. Why else would I want to go into a dang freezin' creek like that? For a bath, huh!"

The other made a rather subtle, knowing grin, which kind of aggravated Hank to see.

"Do you recall the Circus that passed through this part of the Territory the other day, on its way to Deadwood?" the rancher asked.

"Yeah . . ." Hank nodded.

"Well, it happened that they lost somethin'," Alex went on. "Somethin' escaped . . ." Pausing, he handed Hank the daily newspaper, fresh from the press in Deadwood. He pointed a finger at a particular item. "Read there," he instructed.

The headlines Hank saw read: ESCAPED SEAL SPENDS TIME IN CREEK.

"They captured the critter late last night," the rancher grinned.

FOR THOSE IN PERIL

The work of the Royal National Lifeboat Institution is outlined by DAVID FIELDEN

The sea is a hard master. Its moods are infinite, from a placid blue calm to a raging fury of indescribable power that can smash a proud, majestic vessel like a child's toy. Fishermen, born of generations of fishermen, the men who brave the rigours of the northern fishing grounds; Royal and Merchant Navy men, masters of the art of seamanship; yachtsmen, as familiar with the lagoons of the South Sea Isles as with the creeks and bays of our own shores; these, and all who are familiar with the whims of the oceans, can be made helpless in an instant by the might of the sea.

In the face of such potential power, what has man to offer in his own defence? The sea has been described as the 'broadest highway in the world', and too much in the way of trade depends on the sea for men to give way to awe of it. Man has two inherent advantages in the struggle: his courage and ingenuity, and these qualities figure largely in the story of the Royal National Lifeboat Institution.

The aims of the Royal National Lifeboat Institution remain today the same as were stated in the original constitution of over one hundred and forty years ago:

The preservation of human life from shipwreck, help to ships in distress, the succour and support of the rescued, regardless of nationality, rewards to those carrying out rescues and provision for the widows and families of those losing their lives in attempts to save others.

Above:
The Royal National Lifeboat Institution flag.

Opposite page:
A forty-four foot steel lifeboat towing a casualty in heavy seas.

Left:
Sir William Hillary and Thomas Wilson M.P., founders of the R.N.L.I.

Below:
A Life Brigade man in action, 1870.

How the battle began

In the early nineteenth century the Industrial Revolution and the resulting nationwide increase in demands for food, fuel and raw materials had greatly increased shipping activity around the coasts of Britain and commercial and fishing fleets were growing rapidly. At this time too there was a series of savage storms which inflicted heavy losses on coastal shipping. One hundred and sixty-nine vessels were lost in three separate gales which occurred in 1821, 1824, and 1829 on the East coast of England between the Humber and the Tees.

Sir William Hillary, a public figure of the time, announced details of his proposed national life-saving organisation and he managed to engage the support of a Member of Parliament named Thomas Wilson. On the 4th March 1824 Wilson convened a meeting in the City of London Tavern which resulted in the formation of the *National Institution for the preservation of life from shipwreck*. Thirty years later this body changed its title to the *Royal National Lifeboat Institution*.

Today the lifeboat service is busier than ever. As more and more people take to the water for pleasure, so a higher proportion get into difficulties, and the Institution zealously guards its claim never to have failed to answer a call. In 1968, 2294 launches were made, saving a total of 996 lives.

A fighting force

The R.N.L.I. has two arms to its service. One hundred and fifty conventional lifeboats operate from Lifeboat Stations around the British Isles. In addition a number of Inshore Rescue Boats are being introduced—fast, inflatable craft with the advantage of not having to launch from a prepared slipway.

A typical conventional lifeboat is the 'Oakley' Class. Designed specifically to meet the Institution's requirements, the boat is of a self-righting type, achieved by the speedy transfer of water ballast into a righting tank on the port side. When the lifeboat is capsized to starboard she rights herself by going through a roll of 360 degrees.

screw vessels are capable of 14 knots, with a useful range of over 300 miles. All the seats in the boat are fitted with car-type safety belts.

To cope with the strain imposed on the service by the boom in pleasure boating around our shores, the Institution has introduced the Inshore Rescue Boats. These little craft are inflatable dinghies of fifteen feet in length. Usually powered by a 40 hp outboard motor, they can do well over 20 knots, and maintain such speeds for at least two hours. Being of nylon construction the boats are light and easily launched by their two-man crew. They can carry up to eight survivors.

Except for one short period when it

It normally takes six seconds for her to reach the upright position from the moment when she is bottom up. When the boat heels over to port, the transfer of water begins just before the point at which she would otherwise capsize, and by this means returns to the upright.

The cabin of the 'Oakley' is fitted with the latest electronic navigation equipment—radar; medium wave, VHF and UHF radio equipment; echo sounder and radio direction finder. She is powered by two 110 hp diesel engines.

Even the efficient 'Oakley', however, is nowhere near perfect as far as the R.N.L.I. is concerned. Six forty-four foot boats based on an American design have been built. These twin-

received an annual grant from the government, the Institution has relied solely upon voluntary public support to enable it to continue its work—and the public has never failed the service. The cost of running the lifeboat service at peak efficiency is around two million pounds annually, and increasing constantly.

The sea takes its toll

Since its foundation the service has lost 257 crew members in the course of duty.

A major tragedy was the loss of the Longhope boat from the Isle of Hoy in the Orkneys. On the night of Monday, 17th March 1969, the Longhope boat put out in answer to a distress call from a drifting freighter which was

being forced aground by mountainous seas and gale force winds. Radio contact was lost soon after the boat was launched. When dawn came to the wild and desolate seascape, with still no word from the lifeboat, an extensive air and sea search was started. The boat, one of the few not of a self-righting type still in service, was found capsized off Tor Ness on the Isle of Hoy. All hands were lost.

The R.N.L.I. has three medals which it awards for individual acts of gallantry. The gold, for an act in which outstanding courage, skill and initiative have been shown. The silver for an act of outstanding merit. The bronze for an act of conspicuous gallantry and courage.

With its seemingly inexhaustible supplies of human courage and skill, and its readiness to take advantage of technical developments to help it in its work, the Institution enters the Nineteen-Seventies well able to cope with any hazard it may have to face from the ever-fickle sea.

Above:
Lifeboat stations around the British Isles

Top left:
A new type of forty foot lifeboat with a fibre glass hull.

Centre left:
An Inshore Rescue Boat at speed.

Bottom left:
An 'Oakley' Class lifeboat at sea.

Hi, Old Timer!

The oldest inhabitant at Belle Vue Zoo in Manchester is this West African Dwarf Crocodile.

Have you ever been to the zoo? And did you ever wonder as you visited all the animals: "Now which can be the oldest?"

Quite a number of animals live to a ripe old age, especially in zoos, where they are carefully looked after. A lot of zoo directors are aware that chimps and monkeys can catch human ailments, such as colds and coughs. In the past many of the older monkeys have died from pneumonia and tuberculosis. Now they are usually protected from such dangers because armour-plated glass windows are used for their dens, instead of bars or fencing.

No two creatures are alike, and every animal arriving at a zoo has a dossier listing its habits, date of birth or arrival, country of origin, history of health and peculiarities of temperament. Their keepers are always alert

Belle Vue's tigon, Rita, was a very rare animal.

Lions have strong teeth, but sometimes they go bad in old age.

These gibbons escape human ills in their natural state, but in zoos they must be protected from germs.

for health problems that may upset their charges.

At Chester Zoo a difficult operation was performed on George, an old alligator. He had a growth in his mouth, and the vet said it must be removed because the animal was finding it hard to eat.

The vet drugged him so that he could be hauled out of his pool and examined. It was a simple matter cutting out the growth, but the keeper was told to bathe the wound with antiseptic each day.

At first George was reluctant to open his mouth. But after a few tussles with his keeper, the alligator became a model patient. Even after he had completely recovered, he used to climb out of his pool and open his mouth wide when he spotted the keeper.

The oldest inhabitant at Belle Vue Zoo in Manchester is a West African Dwarf Crocodile. It has been at the zoo for twenty-one years, its age on arrival being unknown. This reptile is a very docile specimen which has a small enclosure set aside for it in the tropical pool designed for the much more active American alligators.

Another of Belle Vue's oldest inhabitants died quite recently. She was Rita, and she was a very rare animal called a Tigon, which is the offspring of a tiger and a lioness.

Rita was a very remarkable animal in many respects. A Tigon would not occur in the wild state, of course, and although they are occasionally produced in zoos, she was believed to be the only one in the world for some years.

Lions rest for a day after a kill like this. So zoos have one 'no feeding' day a week.

Rita was one of a pair of Tigons bred in the private zoological collection of the Sultan of Morocco. The two Tigons came to Belle Vue as young adults. The male died shortly after its arrival in this country, but Rita remained a firm favourite in the zoo for many years until her death. Letters were received from all parts of the world seeking information about this most unusual animal.

Rita lived to be much older than was expected. In her latter years she enjoyed the freedom of the new outdoor enclosures in a wooded and secluded corner of Belle Vue.

In their bush and jungle home, giraffes must suffer gumboils in silence. But in zoos they are carefully treated.

One of the oldest inhabitants at Chester Zoo was Punch, the polar bear. He was one of a collection of animals which the zoo took over in 1932. At first he refused to be coaxed into the water. He was the dirtiest, most bedraggled bear imaginable.

Then Punch was given a companion polar bear, Judy. The two were given fine new quarters and a swimming pool. This caused an improvement in their health, and prolonged their lives. When Punch died, it was estimated that he was forty-one years old, a great age for a polar bear, captive or not.

Animals with aches and pains

Many animals suffer from the same troubles that beset humans. When a giraffe gets a gumboil—as some tend to—it is up to the keeper to try to ease the animal's pain.

At Chester Zoo a fifteen-foot giraffe named Maud, from Somaliland, went off her food. She was found rocking her head from side to side.

The keeper brought his ladder, leaned it against the fence and persuaded the giraffe to come close. He soon saw what was wrong. But giving her the hot water mouthwashes prescribed by the vet was a difficult game. Sometimes Maud refused to open her mouth, as the keeper struggled on the top of his ladder with the bucket. Then as he climbed down, the contrary giraffe would rush to the fence and lean over, opening her mouth.

Lions prove themselves to be hardy inhabitants of zoos. Most will only seek the shelter of their dens when it is pouring with rain. They even enjoy rolling in the snow.

In their natural state lions kill, eat and then rest before making another kill. So most zoos have a 'no feeding' day for lions. This is one reason for the splendid health of old lions in zoos. Unfortunately some of the old timers need to have their teeth removed. Then they have their meat chopped up for them, since they can no longer chew it.

Photographs by courtesy of The South African Tourist Corporation

Route to Mount Everest (1953 Everest Expedition).

EVEREST CONQUERED!

Brian Murphy describes some attempts on Everest and the final successful expedition

1933 Everest Expedition Party established at Camp Six.

Mount Everest, in the Himalayan range, and on the frontier between Tibet and Nepal, is the highest mountain in the world. There have been slightly varying estimates of its exact height. While it is generally regarded as being over 29,000 feet high, some have calculated its height at 29,002 feet, and a more recent estimate puts it down at roughly 29,028 feet.

To the people living near, the mountain is called Chomolungma, which means 'Goddess Mother of the World'; the name Everest was given to it in 1858 in honour of Sir George Everest, who was Surveyor-General in India at the time.

The Nepalese and the Tibetan people, living as they did in isolation and having little contact with the outside world, did not much approve of the intrusion of foreign visitors and were not very communicative. Because of this, for many years little was known of Mount Everest.

THE FIRST BRITISH EXPEDITION

In the second half of the nineteenth century, however, mountaineers began tackling the remote country in the Himalayas, but it was not until the end of the First World War that plans were seriously discussed to organise a British expedition.

The Tibetan Government, in 1920, gave permission for a British mountaineering team to explore and map Mount Everest; their ruler assured the team that he would give them any help he could.

There were certain problems that had to be solved. One of the problems was that posed by the conditions with which the men would be faced when climbing at such high altitudes. They would need special clothing, equipment and food supplies if they were to survive.

The winter in Tibet brings a bitterly cold wind which blows southwards across the mountains, making climbing impossible. Summer brings a monsoon from the Bay of Bengal in India, carrying with it heavy rain which turns to snow on reaching the mountains. This soft snow forms avalanches which make climbing hazardous. It was decided, therefore, that the expedition should start in the spring, thus avoiding the winter winds and the summer monsoon.

The great heights posed another problem, that of lack of oxygen. At heights above 18,000 feet it becomes difficult for the body to adjust to the

Ice Needles near Base Camp, Lho la.

Nearing the foot of the icefall, close under Lho la.

conditions, and above heights of 24,000 feet it is impossible for the human body to acclimatise itself. Once at this height, the body becomes weak and enfeebled, and the longer a person stays at this height, the weaker he gets. All the climbers who have ever been to these great heights agree that they felt much weaker.

THE FIRST ATTEMPT

The first attempt on Everest was made when an expedition left Darjeeling, near the northern frontier of India, on 18th May, 1921. The expedition was led by C. K. Howard-Bury, its aim being to make a thorough exploration of the mountain and to choose the best route by which to make an ascent.

Progress was slow and climbing difficult. Mules carried all the food and equipment; the mules were later replaced by yaks and ponies when the expedition crossed higher into Tibet. Eventually the team climbed too high to be able to use even the yaks, and from then on the Sherpas had to shoulder the burden.

The Sherpas are an amazingly strong race of men, originally from the valleys of Nepal; they can carry heavy loads for as long as a whole day. This is no small feat when it is considered that, on average, Sherpas are only about five feet tall!

From Tibet, the expedition worked its way along the north side of Everest. It was agreed, after several weeks of travelling and exploring, that it was possible to climb Everest—by reaching the North Col, which was 23,500 feet high, and then by climbing to the great north-east ridge. Once at that point, they thought that the ascent would be far less difficult.

The expedition returned to England, happy in the knowledge that they had discovered a possible route.

In 1922 a team of twelve people, led by General C. G. Bruce, set off on the second expedition to Mount Everest. They took with them special oxygen cylinders to use when once above the North Col.

On this expedition a height of 27,000 feet was reached by G. L. Mallory, E. F. Norton and T. H. Somervell without using their oxygen cylinders, while G. I. Finch and J. G. Bruce later reached 27,300 feet with the aid of the oxygen. Unfortunately, they were forced to turn back, victims of exhaustion and the extreme cold.

Later, seven Sherpas were tragically killed when an avalanche swept them over an ice-cliff below the North Col.

All further attempts to climb Everest had to be abandoned because of the monsoon, which came at about that time.

FURTHER ATTEMPTS

There were other expeditions to Everest, two more notable ones taking place in 1924 and 1933.

The members of the expedition in 1924 set up two camps above the North Col. These were Camps Five and Six. They also discovered two short, steep sections, known as the first and second step, on the north-east ridge. Norton and Somervell made a point of avoiding these steps by crossing the north face of the mountain on their way to the summit.

Somervell was eventually prevented from going on, as he felt so ill. Norton continued, and finally reached a height of 28,000 feet, but then he too had to return. Norton had managed, however, to go up higher than anyone before him.

Mallory and A. C. Irvine left Camp Six four days later to make their attempt to conquer the mountain.

Mallory had been a member of the previous expeditions and it was his idea to take the route along the ridge. N. E. Odell, another climber, watched them journeying towards the summit, but they eventually disappeared from view, and were never seen again.

Nine years later Hugh Rutledge led another expedition. This expedition set up Camp Six, higher—at 27,400 feet—than any camp before.

L. R. Wager and P. Wyn Harris made the first of their team's attempts on the summit. They had planned to follow the ridge and, if possible, climb the two steps. Along the route they came across Mallory's ice-axe. On reaching the second step they realised that they could not continue along that route, so they tried to cross the mountain face. They managed to reach the Great Couloir, a gully running from below the summit down the centre of the mountain face.

Panorama of three great peaks: Everest, Lhotse and Nuptse.

As night fell, however, they could go no further, and had to return to the camp.

Two other members of the team tried two days later to follow the path Norton had taken previously. They were F. S. Smythe and E. E. Shipton. Shipton hadn't gone very far when he had to turn back. Smythe pressed on as far as the Great Couloir, but here met with such difficulty that he had to turn back. Smythe, Wyn Harris and Wager had reached the same point as Norton did in 1924.

On a later expedition, in 1951, Eric Shipton discovered an approach to Everest from the south side. This was through a glacier-filled hollow called the West Cwm.

THE HUNT EXPEDITION

In 1952, Colonel John Hunt was chosen to lead the British expedition to Mount Everest. His job was to find a suitable team of fit, experienced climbers who would put the success of the expedition before all personal claims to triumph.

His chosen team consisted of climbers from Britain and New Zealand: Charles Evans, Tom Bourdillon, Alfred Gregory, Edmund Hillary, George Lowe, Charles Wylie, Michael Westmacott, George Band, Wilfred Noyce, Michael Ward (the team's doctor), and in addition Griffith Pugh, physiologist sponsored by the Medical Research Council, and Tom Stobart, who was to film the expedition for Countryman Films Ltd.

Before leaving London for Nepal, Colonel Hunt had prepared a plan for the ascent. This plan was drawn up with the most painstaking attention to detail, and every possible hazard was noted.

The plan split the expedition into three parts. The first was to establish an Advance Base inside the West Cwm at 23,000 feet. The second stage entailed setting up an Assault Camp on the South Col. The final stage consisted of the assault, during which teams of four men, comprising two Sherpas and two Europeans, would tackle the summit in turn. The attempt was to be made via the south ridge, rising from the South Col to the summit.

The final stage of Colonel Hunt's plan had to be modified later, but the plan as a whole contributed greatly to the expedition's success. Another important factor in its success was the choice of equipment used. This was specially designed to meet every need. There was clothing which gave protection from the intense cold and a new type of lightweight oxygen apparatus. There were boots specially designed for the expedition, and also radio equipment.

In March 1953, the team met in Katmandu, the capital city of Nepal, and the Advance Base Camp had been established in the West Cwm by mid-May. Then the difficult trek across the Lhotse Mountain brought the expedition to the South Col where Camp Eight was set up on 24th May.

The time was now right for the first attempt on the summit. Bourdillon and Evans were the first to try, on 26th May, but as they went higher up the mountain they found the ridge covered with newly fallen snow. This, together with bad weather conditions and faulty oxygen equipment, made the climb very difficult. They reached the South Peak of Everest, which is 28,700 feet high and only 300 feet below the summit, before being forced to turn back.

The West Cwm—Ferry party on the way to Camp Four.

Any attempt on the summit the next day had to be postponed due to strong winds. The wind was still fierce on 28th May, but the team decided that the next attempt should be made.

HILLARY'S TURN

It was the turn of Edmund Hillary and the Sherpa leader, Tenzing. They were to climb above the South Col and set up camp for the night, as near to the summit as they could get in the time, so that the next day the last lap would be made as easy as possible for them.

On the day that Bourdillon and Evans had made their unsuccessful climb, Colonel Hunt had been up the mountain with a party to deposit food and equipment on the ridge at 27,300 feet. This left considerably less for Hillary, Tenzing and their support party to carry up.

Early on the morning of 28th May, Hillary and Tenzing set out to follow their support party: George Lowe, Alfred Gregory and Sherpa Ang Nyima. They kept to the steps that had been cut by these men. Then they all made their way to the spot where Colonel Hunt had left the extra equipment. Here, they shouldered the extra loads and continued on up the ridge as far as they could manage in the time left, before the support party had to return to the South Col. Hillary and Tenzing pitched their tent on a rocky slope just by the ridge, after digging out two level strips of ground a yard wide and six feet long.

After a night 27,900 feet up, they awoke with the dawn and had breakfast. Then, at 6.30 a.m., they began the last stage of their climb. By 9 a.m. they had reached the summit of the South Peak, and they were a mere 1,200 feet from the summit of Everest.

1953 Everest Expedition party.

Hillary calculated that there was enough oxygen to give them four and a half hours of climbing, then they would be forced to turn back or be stranded without air on that icy ridge.

With the greatest caution the two men slowly made their way along to one of the most difficult obstacles that had to be surmounted—a rock face of forty feet. Hillary realised that there wasn't enough time to tackle it. But then, at one side of the rock face, he spotted a narrow ridge cut between the rock and a bank of snow. So the two men worked their way upwards, keeping their feet on the snow bank and their hands on the rocky ledge. Eventually Hillary managed to pull himself on to the top of the rock face, Tenzing followed and they set off again, cutting steps across the snow ridge. The task was a long and arduous one, but eventually they made it.

THE TOP OF THE WORLD

There they stood—the first two men in the world—on the summit of Mount Everest! They stayed on the summit for about fifteen minutes, scarcely able to contain their joy. They were also very relieved that the whole thing was over.

Hillary took photographs of the view from the top and also of the routes taken by the earlier expeditions. Tenzing buried food and sweets in the snow as a gift to the Buddhist god that the Nepalese believe lives on this great mountain.

Tenzing at the summit of Mount Everest (1953).

Then Hillary took a final photograph of Tenzing holding his ice-axe, attached to which was a string of flags: British, United Nations, Nepalese and Indian.

Hillary buried a crucifix, given to him by John Hunt, in the snow.

Now it was time for them to come down. Although eager to tell the rest of the men the news, they made their way down the mountainside very carefully.

They reached the reserve oxygen cylinders and paused to couple them to their breathing apparatus, then off they went again. The last journey down to the south Col was extremely wearying. When at last they saw George Lowe coming to meet them, they were overwhelmed with happiness and relief. Their oxygen had just about run out.

The joy of their friends when Hillary and Tenzing told them the wonderful news can easily be imagined. There was a marvellous atmosphere of excitement, and much celebration and back-slapping.

Everest was conquered at last, and they were the first to do it. They couldn't wait to spread the news.

The next day, their leader, Colonel Hunt, was informed of their triumph, which also became rapidly known the world over.

Edmund Hillary and John Hunt were knighted for their part in the success of the expedition.

Hillary and Tenzing approaching 28,000 feet at the site of Camp Nine.

AV

It was close on six o'clock in the morning when Hugh Wentworth, a sturdy lad of some sixteen years of age, awoke and, throwing aside the thin blankets which had covered him, scrambled from his bed. Hastily he pulled on a thick jersey and a pair of strong boots, shivering as he felt the cold air of the morning.

He crept quietly down the old stone stairway so as not to wake the rest of the family and, in the small hallway, picked up the parcel of food prepared for his father. He let himself out into the cobbled street, closed the door gently and took a deep breath. The early morning mist from the river had not yet been dispelled and he hurried through the streets of Old Pimlico to keep himself warm.

"Faith, 'tis cold," he muttered to himself as he ran.

At length, he turned out of the slush and mud of the street and ran down the sloping way lined with fishing sheds to where the stairs jutted out into the river. At the foot of the stairs a small rowboat lay tied up and in it he could see by the light of the street lantern the burly figure of his father.

"Ah, son," said John Wentworth. "It has been a cold night on the river. I shall be glad to get some vittles inside me."

"Yes, father," said Hugh, handing over the parcel. "I am glad too that I have done my errand and can return to the warmth of the house."

"Good boy," said his father, clapping him on his back. He stepped back into the boat and picked up the oars. "Tell your mother I shall be home at noon."

"Aye, father, that I will," said

WARNING FOR PYM

by W. K. Watts

A story of turbulent days in England's history

Hugh and hurried up the stairs.

He paused at the top to wave to his father, who was pulling strongly at the oars. The exercise had warmed him and, now that there was no need to keep his father waiting, he made his way more slowly up the sloping street from the river.

As he drew near the fishing sheds he paused. What was that sound he heard? It sounded like a groan and he listened intently. There it was again, and this time he had no doubt that it was a human voice that had made it. It came from one of the sheds and he moved forward until, at length, the anguished sound rose up to him almost at his feet.

He bent forward, his eyes searching the darkness, and it was then he saw the figure of a man lying crumpled up in the shadow of one of the huts. The silk stockings, buckled shoes and long cloak told him at once that this was no tramp moaning in his misery, but a gentleman in some distress.

"What is it sir?" Hugh demanded, leaning forward.

"Help me to sit up, boy," came the croaked reply, and Hugh put his arm gently round the man's shoulders and raised his head.

"You're wounded, sir," gasped Hugh, as he saw the ugly red patch which stained the tunic.

"Aye, unto death," muttered the man.

"Rest quietly. I will find a doctor."

But the man restrained him with a fierce whisper and an even more urgent clutch of a feeble hand. "'Tis too late. No doctor can save me now."

"But who did such a foul deed?"

"One of Charles' men. I know not who he was, but he caught me by surprise."

Hugh frowned. The City of London was full of turmoil and trouble. The king's men were becoming more and more demanding, so that the common people were being steadily driven towards civil war. Parliament itself was rising against him and it was plain, even to a boy like Hugh, that there could be but one outcome to the struggle.

Charles believed, even more so than his father James I, that because he was king he could do no wrong, that he was above all the laws of the land and could rule just as he wished, and so he levied taxes and imprisoned anyone who dared go against him.

Hugh's thoughts were broken by the mutterings of the man who leaned so weakly against his arm.

"He suspected who I was, and used his sword to silence me." There was a gasping pause. "But he failed."

"But who are you, sir?" asked Hugh. "Why will you not allow me to seek help?"

"'Tis too late, I tell you. And it matters not who I am. Not who I am, but what I am."

"I understand not," said Hugh in a puzzled voice.

He stared down at the man in the gloom and, for a moment, thought he had died, so still he lay. But in a moment, he took a long breath and continued in the same hurried laboured speech.

"I am a messenger. I carry a message for John Pym and his friends."

"Yes, sir?"

"'Tis urgent. 'Tis deadly urgent. Their lives—depend on't. In my pocket you will find a paper."

He gestured feebly and Hugh put his hand in to the side pocket of his tunic and brought forth a rolled piece of paper tied with a cord.

"This message, sir?"

The half closed eyes rolled slowly towards the scroll and his head moved forward in a barely noticeable nod.

"Aye, that's it," came the hushed voice. "Take it—to Parliament. Deliver it—to Pym. Or Hampden. Now. Today. You understand?"

"Aye, sir, I understand."

"You will—do it? You swear?"

"Aye, sir. I swear."

A faint little smile curved the man's lips. He moved once, as if to settle himself more comfortably.

"Good—lad."

His voice was but a breath on the damp air, and then his head fell forward and his whole body relaxed. Hugh took his arm gently from around the man's shoulders and eased him to the ground. He stood up and his lips set grimly as he looked down.

"God rest your soul," he said, and stepped out from behind the fishing shed.

His eyes rested on the message clutched in his hand. "Take it to Parliament," the man had said. "Deliver it to Pym. Or Hampden. Their lives depend on it." He moved round the corner of the fishing shed and began running.

His thoughts were troubled as he ran. He did not know when Parliament began its business for the day. John Pym he knew by sight, as many dwellers in London did, but not Hampden.

He left the riverside and turned right along the long road that led

63

past Lambeth Bridge. He knew that John Pym, a countryman and a lawyer, was well loved and much admired for his oratory. He had done much to force Charles to sign the Petition of Right which laid down that it was not lawful for even a king to make people pay taxes without the consent of Parliament, or to put people in prison unless they had been properly tried and it had been proved that they had broken the law. But even after he had signed the Petition, Charles had continued in his old arrogant way.

So occupied was he with his thoughts that he was greatly alarmed when a figure suddenly stepped out of an alleyway and seized him by his collar.

"Hold it, young sir," he exclaimed. "Why were you running at such a pace at this hour of the morning?"

"'Twas nothing, sir," said Hugh in great confusion. "I was but hurrying to be home for breakfast."

"A likely story," snorted the man, a stout middle-aged figure clad in severe garments. "Why should you be about the streets at all? You are running away—from what, I wonder."

"No, sir," protested Hugh, struggling wildly to release himself.

"A thief, perhaps, running from the scene of his crime."

"No, sir, I am not a thief."

"What is that you hold clutched so tightly in your hand then?"

Hugh looked down at the precious paper and his efforts to free himself redoubled.

"'Tis nothing, sir. 'Tis but a message I have to deliver."

"A message, eh? Give it to me that I may read. Give it to me, I say."

He spun Hugh round and with his free hand jerked the paper from him. Clumsily he attempted to unroll it and at length succeeded sufficiently to read a few words.

"To Master John Pym," he gasped, and so astounded was he that he released Hugh so as to have both hands free.

He moved over to the wall where a street lantern flickered and Hugh saw his chance in the man's deep concern. He sprang forward and snatched at the paper frantically and, to his joy, regained it. Then he turned and fled as fast as he could.

As he ran he heard the man shout after him, but Hugh laughed to himself. That stout figure could never catch him, and after he had covered some two hundred yards he paused to catch his breath and to listen if there were any sound of pursuit.

But what he heard sent him shrinking back into the shadows, for what fell on his ears was not the laboured footsteps of the stout gentleman but the clatter of a horse's hooves.

Hugh stared fearfully as the horse drew abreast of him, and his heart gave a jump of relief as he saw that the rider was tall and slim and looked not at all like the portly gentleman. He was richly garbed and there was the finest lace in his collar and his cuffs. Hugh stepped from his hiding place, but the horseman must have seen him for he pulled up his steed with a jerk. He flung himself from his saddle with an easy movement and, holding the reins with his left hand, drew his sword.

"How now, sirrah," he said in a biting tone and raised his sword so that its point touched Hugh's chest. "Why, 'tis the rogue I seek."

"I know not what you mean, sir," said Hugh in alarm.

"Methinks you do. You carry a message given you by a villain. I crossed swords with him back at the fishing sheds yonder."

"Crossed swords?" flared Hugh. "That gentleman carried no sword. You killed him in cold blood."

"Careful, my coxcomb. Throw your message to me and take care how you do it, or my sword will play its part again."

His arm moved upward and the sword point pricked Hugh's throat, so that in despair he tossed the message to the man's feet. Warily the Rider stooped, dragging the horse's head forward so that he could pick up the paper with his left hand.

"To Master John Pym," he read. "Save us," he cried. "The plan is known."

Hugh was filled with a fury he had never known before. In spite of the threat of the sword point, he stepped back lightly and snatched up a loose cobble stone.

"Murderer," he shouted and flung it with all his strength.

The heavy missile struck the man in his chest so that he staggered back with a yell of pain, his arms waving wildly in the air. Once again Hugh plucked the message from helpless fingers and he spun round and darted up the alleyway.

Pursuit this time would be a different matter. A vengeful horseman would soon run him down in spite of his fleetness of foot. Skill and cunning must come to his aid if he were to deliver the message safely, which he was now more determined than ever to do. Fortunately he was well acquainted with the district and he pressed forward quickly through small alleys and byways that no horseman could traverse.

Again and again he heard the sound of hooves, whether of his pursuer or another he knew not, and he cowered down until they had passed. But all the time he moved on steadily towards Westminster. The time was passing more swiftly than he cared to think about, but he dare not risk his safety and the success of his mission. The greatest danger would come, he knew, when he would have to emerge from the shelter of the buildings into the open space that stood before the House of Parliament.

At length, he reached the end of the last alleyway. He realised he had not heard the ominous clatter of horses' hooves for some minutes, and he felt a little throb of relief at the thought that he might have put his pursuer off the scent.

He moved to the corner of the last building of the row he had been creeping along and looked round. There were people about, but they looked like honest folks intent on their business. Nowhere could he see the man on horseback. Ahead of him were the gates he must reach. Once within the courtyard behind the gate he felt he would be safe. How far away were they, he wondered. A

hundred yards, but it looked like a mile.

He took a deep breath and ran. He ran as he had never run before, stepping aside lightly to avoid the passers-by, swerving this way and that. The gates were fifty yards away, twenty, ten, and then as he stretched out his arms to touch them, a man sprang out before him with drawn sword, and Hugh came to a halt with a sob in his throat. To have got so close and then to be foiled. He moved to one side and then another, and each time the sword point flickered at his throat.

"You are in a hurry, you young villain," drawled the man with a sneer. "I knew you would come here, and 'twas an easy matter to forestall

you. Hand over my property and I shall take no further action."

"Your property?" gasped Hugh, and looked round wildly.

One or two people were gazing at the scene with curious eyes. They would be thinking that the richly dressed man had caught a thief, and Hugh felt he would receive scant help from them. But he would not give up his trust so easily. He opened his mouth to shout and the sword point moved upwards. Then an iron hand fell on his shoulder.

"What goes on here?" demanded a stern voice.

Hugh turned his head and, to his horror, found himself gazing at the plump face of the stout gentleman he had met earlier. Now, indeed, all was lost. He struggled furiously to release himself, but the grip on his

shoulder was too strong. His captor had been joined, too, by several companions. It was more than he could stand and he sagged helplessly, feeling beyond any more effort.

"Fear not, lad," said the man.

Hugh could hardly believe his ears. He looked up and, to his amazement, found that the man was smiling.

"I am a friend of John Pym," he said quietly, and turned his gaze sternly at the man with the sword. "Out of our way, sirrah, or 'twill be the worse for you," and he and his companions moved forward purposefully, taking Hugh with them.

Faced with such odds, the cavalier put up his sword and, shrugging his shoulders, stepped aside to allow them to pass within the gates.

"Now, the message, lad."

Hugh looked round the circle of faces and felt a surge of confidence in what he saw. He handed over the precious paper without a word and saw it unrolled and hastily read by all the men. Then he saw the stout man beckon a messenger.

"Take this to Master Pym or Master Hampden as fast as you can. Delay nothing. Precious lives depend on't."

"Aye, sir," said the messenger, touching his hat and speeding off.

"Know you its contents?" asked the man, and Hugh shook his head. "Then I will tell you. 'Tis a warning that King Charles, openly breaking the law, is to come today, with soldiers, to arrest Master Pym and four others who have spoken against his injustices. By your skill and bravery, they have been warned in time. We shall arrange for them to leave the House and make for the river and so into the City of London where the King dare not follow them. Now, get you gone. Beware of yon cavalier on your way from here, although methinks he will not trouble you again. And for your trouble, take this crown piece. 'Tis small payment for the saving of such lives."

Hugh thanked them and told them where they might find the body of the messenger. Then, clutching his crown piece, he was led to the gate and needed no further urging to hurry home as fast he could.

Contraband Cargoes

The smugglers by Morland (c. 1800)

A HISTORY OF SMUGGLERS AND SMUGGLING

"A smuggler is a person who . . . would have been, in every respect an excellent citizen had not the laws of his country made that a crime which Nature never meant to be so."

Adam Smith
Philosopher and Economist

A thick damp mist adds to the gloom of the heavy moonless night and deadens the sound of the flowing tide slithering over invisible pebbles. High on the cliff-top overlooking the bay a cloaked figure calms his nervous horse and flashes a spout lantern into the darkness. Far into the mist another light flickers an answer, and minutes later the ghostly shape of a rowing-boat looms out of the darkness.

Swiftly and silently men scramble from the craft and heap their cargo of casks and chests onto the shore. The cliff watcher leads his cart down to the water's edge and the barrels are heaved onto the back. The men chat for a moment; money changes hands; the cart rumbles off into the night, bound for London, and the sailors row with muffled oars back to the cutter moored out in the bay.

Another night's smuggling successfully accomplished. A few hundred pounds worth of duty-free goods out of the millions that were run into similar hidden coves every year. At the height of Britain's smuggling era, during the fifteenth and sixteenth centuries, the amount of imports that were slipped secretly into the country far outweighed those goods on which duty had been paid.

INTRODUCTION OF TAXES

The smuggler first appeared in history towards the end of the thirteenth century, when King Edward I became concerned about the financial state of his realm, and levied taxes on a national basis on such imports and exports as wool, cloth and wines. England was not a rich country and the merchants and ordinary citizens, enraged at the taxes which were placed on more and more commodities every year, naturally turned to smuggling.

To all except the Revenue Officers, smuggling was not considered a crime, and even the most honest of men thought nothing of cheating the king of his taxes. The law, of course, regarded the smuggler as a criminal, but for Englishmen as a whole he was simply an honest thief whose exploits were applauded, envied and imitated.

In 1275 a permanent staff of Customs officials was created, but it took many years for an efficient preventive service to take shape. It was not until the fifteenth century that Customs cutters began to patrol the estuaries in an attempt to eradicate smuggling. About the same time 'tide waiters', which were Customs vessels waiting on the tide, began to board ships bound for London at Gravesend to prevent any unauthorised landing of goods. But for the whole of the English coastline there were only three of these vessels. There were also the 'land waiters' and the Riding Officers or *gobloos* as they were called by smugglers—to patrol the coastal roads. But again their numbers were pitifully few and their task gigantic.

But in the early days of the Customs officials the smugglers or 'free-traders' soon learned of a safe and relatively simple method of avoiding the duty on their goods: bribes. For a small sum of money or a share of the contraband, most officials could be persuaded to turn a blind eye to the smugglers' activities. A bribe was much cheaper than paying the duty on the goods, and merchants felt that paying a small sum to an official was much easier than the bother of running the contraband onto some remote shore.

The government became increasingly aware of the corruption in the Customs Service, but was virtually powerless for many years to put an end to it. Officers were appointed to watch the land-waiters, but they in their turn fell prey to bribery, and more officers were appointed to watch *them*. It was alleged that once a man was appointed to even the humblest office in the London Customs, he was made for life. The wages of the Customs officers were incredibly low, but practically everyone employed in the service could afford to live the life of lords.

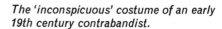

The 'inconspicuous' costume of an early 19th century contrabandist.

IN MANY DISGUISES

But when bribery was not possible, on the rare occasions that an honest official was on duty, the cunning smuggler had many tricks with which to outwit the Customs officers. Reforms in the Customs service were frequent, but with each one smugglers became more daring and simply found more loopholes.

Successfully disguising the contraband was the essence of smuggling. Ships were often boarded and searched by the Customs officers, and though they carried fortunes in contraband the goods went undiscovered, they were so well hidden or disguised.

Wines, oils and linen were brought into the country in barrels of onions and apples. Jars of spirits dumped on beaches were camouflaged as rocks. Oilskin bags of tea were thrown overboard and anchored, and looked like innocent mackerel and lobster pots.

As time went on, the smugglers' tricks became even more ingenious. They delighted in laying false trails for the Riding Officers, and often a man with a lantern would be detached from a smuggling gang and allow himself to be caught, carrying casks which contained only sea-water, while his companions further down the coast ran in the true contraband unhindered.

Once, in the 18th century, elaborate arrangements were made at Dover to receive the coffin of an English lady who had 'passed away' in France. The coffin came ashore with proper dignity, was placed in a hearse drawn by six horses, accompanied by two coaches of mourners, and left for London at funeral pace. This story became a great joke among the smugglers of that time, for the coffin was packed with the finest French lace.

One of the smugglers' more brazen tricks was to sail up the River Tyne in the midst of a fleet of colliers, which were never approached by Customs ships. In this way they could travel inland without even being seen. Less daring captains would simply transfer their contraband to a collier out at sea, and the coal ship would sail back to its port unchallenged.

Other devious methods of foxing the Customs Officers were to roll tobacco into balls, cover them with a protective skin and then a covering of clay, so that they resembled potatoes; then precious stones were concealed in kegs of butter, silks and lace in the false bottoms of hen-coops and hollow sides of egg boxes. Perfume was even smuggled in mock champagne bottles, complete with the characteristic wiring around their necks.

For many years smugglers succeeded in humiliating the officers of the Customs service, as well as making fortunes for themselves. There is a famous story in Sussex concerning smugglers and the Revenue men. One night, a group of rustics were standing around a pond trying to rake up some kegs of rum and brandy which had been dumped into the water by a fleeing smuggler. When a party of Revenue officers caught them, the men pretended to be silly and stupid and told the officers that they were raking in the moon's reflection, and the contraband was saved. The joke spread all over England and to this day we have the name 'moonraker', meaning a crazy person.

In the latter half of the seventeenth century smuggling was still the main livelihood of many English citizens. At this time tea was the money-maker for England's smugglers. Tea, in fact, was the most profitable black market commodity that ever existed. The East India Company possessed the sole monopoly and tea prices were ridiculously high. But because of the huge amounts that were smuggled into the country, England fast became the tea-drinking nation that it is today. Smug-

Well out of sight of the feared Customs cutter a night's haul is unloaded and hidden deep inside a cave.

gling even created new industries, such as the manufacture of the special oilskin bags in which tea was invariably smuggled.

THE NEW MORALITY

But now the image of the smuggler was gradually changing. There was an increasing difficulty in finding loopholes in the customs laws, and so the smugglers formed themselves into armed gangs, and made no secret of their dealings; anyone who tried to stop them was beaten or killed.

With the advent of John and Charles Wesley and the Methodists, the gradual decline of smuggling began. Wesley's Nonconformist preaching revolutionised public morality and the smuggler, once a hero of the people, was now thought of as robbing the community as a whole, as well as the government.

In 1846, Great Britain became committed to a policy of free trade, and in 1850 all export duties had been abolished and very few import duties remained. Smuggling now became relatively unimportant, and the days of the swashbuckling 'unfair trader' in three-cornered hat and long sea-boots, wading ashore at midnight laden with casks of brandy, were numbered.

Half a league, half a league,
  Half a league onward,
All in the valley of Death
  Rode the six hundred.
"Forward, the Light Brigade!
Charge for the guns!" he said:
Into the valley of Death
  Rode the six hundred.

"Forward, the Light Brigade!"
Was there a man dismay'd?
Not tho' the soldier knew
  Some one had blunder'd:
Their's not to make reply,
Their's not to reason why,
Their's but to do and die,
Into the valley of Death
  Rode the six hundred.

Cannon to right of them,
Cannon to left of them,
Cannon in front of them
  Volley'd and thunder'd;
Storm'd at with shot and shell,
Boldly they rode and well,
Into the jaws of Death,
Into the mouth of Hell
  Rode the six hundred.

Flash'd all their sabres bare,
Flash'd as they turn'd in air,
Sabring the gunners there,
Charging an army, while
  All the world wonder'd:
Plunged in the battery-smoke
Right thro' the line they broke;
Cossack and Russian
Reel'd from the sabre-stroke
  Shatter'd and sunder'd.
Then they rode back, but not,
  Not the six hundred.

Cannon to right of them,
Cannon to left of them,
Cannon behind them
  Volley'd and thunder'd;
Storm'd at with shot and shell,
While horse and hero fell,
They that had fought so well
Came thro' the jaws of Death
Back from the mouth of Hell,
All that was left of them,
  Left of six hundred.

When can their glory fade?
O the wild charge they made!
  All the world wonder'd.
Honour the charge they made!
Honour the Light Brigade.
  Noble six hundred!

ALFRED, LORD TENNYSON

THE CHARGE OF THE LIGHT BRIGADE

Brian Murphy outlines the background behind Tennyson's immortal poem

This moving poem by Tennyson, published in 1854, was written in honour of the noble and courageous men who rode unquestioningly to an almost certain death in Balaclava during the Crimean War. The cruel fate of these brave men made a deep and lasting impression on Tennyson and this famous poem served to immortalise them.

The Crimean War was fought between Russian forces and the allied armies of England, France, Sardinia and Turkey. The immediate cause was a dispute between France, Russia and Turkey about the control of the Holy Places in Jerusalem. But the true underlying reasons for the outbreak were commercial and political and far more complex.

War broke out in 1853 when the Russians occupied the provinces of Moldavia and Wallachia, which were under Turkish control.

In March 1854 Britain and France declared war on Russia. An allied army landed in the Russian peninsula to attack Sevastopol, the Russian naval base. The allies defeated the Russians at the battle of the Alma River and decided to attack Sevastopol from the south. But in the delay the Russians strengthened their defences.

The blunders of Balaclava

In October 1854 the Allies were attacked by the Russians in the battle of Balaclava. The Allies won but during this battle the suicidal Charge of The Light Brigade was made.

A series of blunders and misunderstandings prior to the charge were destined to bring about catastrophe.

The Heavy Brigade had chased the Russians from the field with a loss of only seventy-eight men. It was a magnificent performance, but unfortunately the men were not allowed to follow it through. Cardigan refused to let any of his men move without permission from Lord Raglan, the Commander-in-Chief.

This was a grave error. The Russians had been forced back and should have been attacked while they were still in a state of confusion.

As it was they were able to get away across the Causeway Heights and position their guns at the bottom of the North Valley.

Now the Russian troops on the Causeway Heights had become separated from the main body of the Russian army.

Lord Raglan saw his chance to recapture his redoubts and with them the road to Balaclava.

Raglan sent an order to Lucan which caused great confusion. He said that the cavalry were to advance and try to recover the Heights. They would be supported by infantry, which had been ordered to advance on two fronts.

Lord Lucan thought that Lord Raglan wanted him to advance *after* the infantry had come to support him. So Lucan positioned the Light Brigade at the top of the North Valley and the Heavy Brigade on the slopes behind them. Then he awaited the arrival of the supporting infantry.

Meanwhile Raglan was waiting for the attack to begin.

The Russians were leaving the field and taking their guns away. Still the attack had not started.

Raglan told General Airey to send Lucan another message. Airey did so. The message read: *Lord Raglan wishes the cavalry to advance rapidly to the front—follow the enemy and try to prevent them from carrying away the guns. Troop Horse Artillery may accompany. French cavalry is on your left. Immediate.*

Nolan, one of the General's aides-de-camp, was sent off speedily to deliver the message and to tell Lord Lucan to attack immediately.

This time, thought Raglan, Lucan could not fail to obey.

From his position, Raglan could see the horses approaching the redoubts and the guns waiting to be dragged away.

But he was much higher up than Lucan, and to Lucan and his troops seven hundred feet below the redoubts appeared empty, and the only guns in danger of being taken away were those of the Russians chased away by the Heavy Brigade and now established at the bottom end of the North Valley in front of them.

It was a fatal mistake.

Nolan, the aide, watched as Lucan

read the message and decried Raglan for wanting him to charge the enemy a mile away to stop them moving their own guns from the bottom of the North Valley.

He hesitated and looked at these guns, the only ones in sight from his position. As he hesitated Nolan flew into a rage, saying that Raglan's order was to attack at once.

Lucan also became angry. "Attack, sir, attack what?" he roared out. "What guns, sir?"

Nolan threw out a hand in an angry movement, which seemed to Lucan to indicate the guns at the end of the North Valley. But it is probable that Nolan, in his anger, was merely gesticulating. Whether he knew Lord Raglan's wishes or not his rage led him to give the wrong directions which brought the Light Brigade to its doom.

Lord Lucan had no choice but to obey the order. He informed Lord Cardigan of the order and told him to advance down the valley with the Light Brigade; he would follow with the Heavy Brigade.

Cardigan queried the order, protesting that the Russians had a battery on their front and batteries and riflemen on each side. But there was nothing that either of them could do.

Into the valley of Death

Cardigan mustered his troops and drew up his brigades into two lines: the first consisting of the 13th Light Dragoons, the 11th Hussars and the 17th Lancers. The second line consisted of the 4th Light Dragoons and the 8th Hussars.

Lucan moved the 11th Hussars behind the first line, to make three lines in all.

Cardigan took his place at the head of his staff and the lines; then he gave the order: "The Brigade will advance."

The Light Brigade was not at full strength, the five regiments could only muster six hundred and seventy-three men, and both of the first lines were led by only Captains; Captain Morris, with his friend Nolan, the aide, leading one of them.

The North Valley was one and a quarter miles long and was very narrow.

On the Fedioukine Hills were the Russian cavalry, infantry and fourteen guns. On the Causeway Heights were more Russian infantry with thirty guns and a field battery.

At the end of the valley facing the Light Brigade was a vast mass of Russian cavalry drawn up into three groups, their twelve guns waiting in front to fire and six more squadrons of Lancers in support.

For all their doubts, and the certain knowledge that they were riding into a trap, the Light Brigade rode bravely on.

Captain Morris complained to Nolan of the long ride and said that they would have been better attacking the guns on the Causeway Heights. Nolan immediately realised that something was wrong and wondered if they were attacking the wrong guns.

Panic-stricken, Nolan moved out of his position and rode quickly to the front where Lord Cardigan was leading the Brigade. But before he had time to warn him the first Russian shell from the Fedioukine Hills burst near him, killing him instantly.

Cardigan thought that Nolan had gone mad when he rode to the front, so he ignored it and continued leading the Brigade down the valley.

All the world wondered

Raglan watched the men advancing roughly towards the redoubts. When they did not turn to attack the Russians he realised that they were heading down the valley and he cried out to Airey in dismay: "There are guns on both sides."

The Russians, too, were amazed—was this little Brigade going to attack the battery at the end of the valley?

There was silence as the proud Brigade advanced.

Then from every side rifles and guns fired down on the Light Brigade.

Men and horses fell, but Cardigan held his men in check. As men died, the riders on each side moved out to avoid being brought down too, and then closed with perfect discipline.

A dreadful mistake had obviously been made, but there was something magnificent about the army riding so bravely to its doom.

The front line was now nearing the battery at the end of the valley, and the firing from the flank was shooting down half a troop at a time.

The pace of the Light Brigade increased, the Heavy Brigade found it impossible to keep up with Cardigan.

When the Heavies began to come under the fierce cross-firing that was carving up the Light Brigade, Lucan saw that he was in danger of losing all the Heavy Brigade as well.

Just then one of the aides was shot dead and Lucan was hit in the leg by a musket ball, while his horse was struck in two places.

ALFRED LORD TENNYSON

Alfred Tennyson was born on April 6, 1809, at Somersby Rectory, Lincolnshire, in the heart of the Fen country, which he always remembered throughout his life. His early life at Somersby was pleasant; there was no lack of money or companionship.

He received his education partly at home and partly at the nearby grammar school at Louth. His two elder brothers were gifted poetically, and Alfred was brought up in an atmosphere of poetry. They were taught Latin and Greek by their father and introduced to all the great English poets.

When Tennyson went up to Cambridge in 1828 he was already regarded as a young man of promise because of a volume of poems published the previous year called *Poems by Two Brothers*.

He was a handsome young man with an athletic physique, and at Cambridge he associated with a group of young men, many of whom filled important positions in later life. One of the most important members of this group was Arthur Henry Hallam. He was regarded as one of the outstanding young men of his generation.

A deep friendship grew up between Hallam and Tennyson. This friendship continued after they both left Cambridge and the relationship became even closer when Hallam became engaged to Tennyson's sister.

Hallam died in 1833, and his death came as a great shock to Tennyson, who was profoundly affected as a result of it. He wrote an elegy, *In Memoriam*, to his friend, upon which he worked for nearly twenty years. When *In Memoriam* appeared, in 1850, Tennyson was soon regarded as the great poet of Victorian England.

On the death of Wordsworth he was made Poet Laureate, and honours were heaped upon him. Many great men of the day became his friends. In 1883 he was made Lord Tennyson. He died in 1892 and was buried in Westminster Abbey.

His life was tranquil and successful and this atmosphere of calm happiness permeates his verse. His poems bring us, as it were, into a lovely garden where everything is carefully tended.

But it is interesting to note that Tennyson, who seemed to lead so quiet a life, wrote some of the best war poems in the English language. One of these was *The Charge of the Light Brigade*, which describes so vividly the disaster of Balaclava.

Lucan saw that the first line of the Heavy Brigade had received many casualties. The Light Brigade was lost, and he knew that he would lose the Heavy Brigade if they kept up the advance.

He ordered the Heavy Brigade to "about turn" and to take up a position where they could protect the Light Brigade on their return.

As the Light Brigade headed nearer to the guns, two brigades of French infantry and two regiments of Chasseurs d'Afrique, led by General Morris, attacked the Russian batteries on the Fedioukine Hills on the opposite side of the valley to Lucan. His men forced the Russians to retreat; now the Light Brigade would have to suffer gunfire from only one side of the valley on their return.

But by now the Light Brigade was reduced to little groups of men lashing their horses to escape the fire and get to grips with the enemy at the end of the valley.

Finally there were so few men left alive that the only order that could be given was "Close in on the centre! Close in!"

It was only a few minutes since the Light Brigade had started its advance and now Lord Cardigan was within a few yards of the Russian guns. Then a burst of firing ripped into the remains of the first line.

A strange silence fell over the valley, and the only thing that the Heavy Brigade could see was an occasional riderless horse, or a wounded man staggering out of the smoke.

About fifty men were still left out of the first line's two regiments, and they were fighting the grey-clad figures with their swords, amongst the guns. To their left Captain Morris and a battery of twenty Lancers fought with several squadrons of Russian Hussars. They forced the Russians to retreat, until a mass of Cossacks appeared and Morris's men were driven back.

Meanwhile, the Russians were being attacked by the first line; on the left was Colonel Mayow and his men, and on the right Lord Paget and his men. The Russians were forced to give way and hide beneath the gun-carriages.

The Light Brigade, having silenced the guns, pressed forward until another mass of Russians appeared before them, and a body of Russian Lancers began to form up behind the Brigade to stop their retreat. Lord Paget ordered his men to wheel and retreat.

Cardigan had been the first man to the guns, but he did not consider it his job to fight among the private soldiers and he rode on until he came to a mass of Russian cavalry headed by Prince Radziville.

The Prince recognised Cardigan and ordered two Cossacks to take him alive as a prisoner. But Cardigan brushed them aside and, turning, rode back through the guns again.

It never occurred to Cardigan to help the wounded, or to try to find his men and lead a retreat. Instead he rode slowly alone back through the valley, trying hard to appear unafraid as firing from the Causeway Heights whistled all around him.

But not the six hundred

Those remaining of the Light Brigade tried to find Lord Cardigan but, on receiving the order to retreat, they bravely rode straight at the Russian lines. The Russians, uncertain as ever, offered little resistance, and without losing one of the small group of desperate survivors, the Light Brigade slipped past into the open.

It was a sad sight as the troops formed their lines back in the safety of Lord Lucan's camp. Out of nearly seven hundred men who had ridden so bravely down the valley only one hundred and ninety-five returned. Nearly five hundred horses were dead, and as a force the Light Brigade no longer existed.

The lesson of Balaclava

Whose fault was it? Perhaps the real blame lay with the army system, where experienced officers were ignored and inexperienced men with titles were able to secure positions of leadership by purchase.

The rest of the men had not been trained properly, so that men like Airey and Nolan did not know how to make clear their leaders' thoughts when it was important to do so.

"There are no bad soldiers—only bad officers." This was proved without a doubt at Balaclava.

THE WILDERNESS THAT ONCE WAS EARTH

The two boys halted at the crackling blue curtain of nothingness and Tim Wells pulled at the arm of Paul Barlow. "Take it easy, Paul," he said, warningly, "you know what the law is and what happens to anyone who breaks it."

"Bosh!" Paul snorted. "What *does* happen? There's never been any record of anyone being punished for going through it."

"There's never been any record of anyone ever coming back so that they *could* be punished," was Tim's reply.

The blue, shimmering Force Field had been around the little town ever since the boys could remember. In fact, to think back to the time when there had been no barrier they needed to go back to their history books, to that time in 1998 when the first starship *Pioneer* had returned to Earth. It had returned earlier than had been expected, for the astronauts had timed their return to coincide with the opening of the Second Millennium in the year 2000. But with the stardrive hurling the ships at 40,000 miles per second through the void, their calculations had been a little off the beam. Amidst the general rejoicings few had bothered. But those rejoicings had lasted for only three days.

The first deaths occurred only three days after *Pioneer* had landed. Salisbury Plain was the great rocket

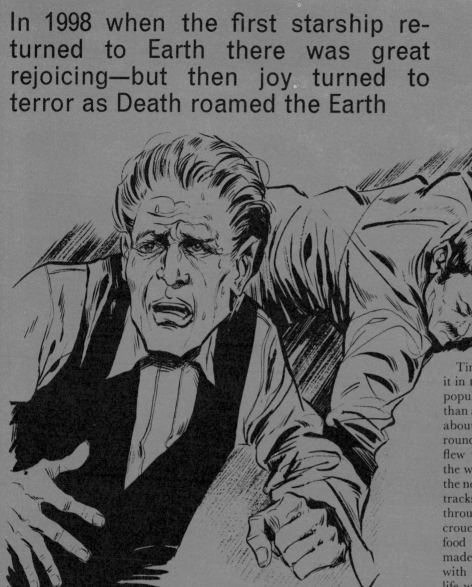

In 1998 when the first starship returned to Earth there was great rejoicing—but then joy turned to terror as Death roamed the Earth

base for Britain, and the first mysterious deaths occurred in the city grown up round the Base.

Three men had ridden *Pioneer* across the gulf between Sun and Alpha Centauri, and these three heroes were the first to die.

That was the first mystery. If the ship had unwittingly carried a plague that was deadly to Earth organisms, why had it left them immune during the long eight-year trip back to Earth? The deaths had spread outward from Salisbury Plain and it was not until five thousand people had died that the Force Field was set up around the Base, and the Base itself sealed off and abandoned. And the menace was still unknown.

The Force Field in those days was a weak, experimental one and the plague, whatever it was, was not contained in Salisbury Plain. It spread, like an invisible menace. It spread over Great Britain and abroad. Whenever a rocket left Britain, as soon as it landed anywhere, the deaths began. Within six months it was worldwide and men everywhere were frantically improving the Force Field which, when perfected, proved to be the only thing that could stop whatever it was that had stricken the Earth. Ironically, men now found themselves prisoners in their own cities while, outside the blue shimmering haze, the invisible foes held Earth in a tight grip.

Tim and Paul had read all about it in the history books. How the total population of Earth, down to less than a hundred millions, lived in only about two hundred cities scattered round the globe. No rockets or planes flew through the calm, sunlit air of the world. No trains or cars travelled the now overgrown roads and railway tracks, and no ships now ploughed through the empty oceans. Men crouched now in their cities; lived on food grown in hydroponic tanks or made in laboratories; communicated with each other by radio only; and life went on, at a reduced pace, but nevertheless it went on. And every branch of scientific research was devoted to trying to understand what had smitten the world, and planning steps to overcome the menace so that men could once more reclaim their lost world.

"But there's nothing out there except jungle," objected Paul, as the two boys squatted down and stared at the blue haze stretching up for five miles into the sky. "Just empty jungle. At first the animals went wild, the dogs turned into things like wolves, and the cats into little tigers. Then they, too, died. And all the time there was nothing to see and not a sound to be heard. It's gruesome, you know. There's nothing there, and yet if anyone went outside everybody says

cover that, although the Things were electrical, yet they did have 'bodies,' at least a framework or something that could move, and that it could vibrate itself out of the vision of men."

Tim got up and the two boys began to walk back towards the little town. As they walked they stared back once or twice at the blue barrier. Few people now went near it. All attempts had long since been given up at trying to find an answer to the problem, and in all those years no one ever saw a single one of the Invaders.

"You know," said Paul suddenly. "It isn't the first time I've thought this, but we've all gone soft. We've stopped *trying*. We've just sat down and let those unknown Things imprison us in these wretched villages we call 'cities'. Why, the pictures of the cities of the old world sixty years ago should be enough to fire anyone's blood."

"Hush, for heaven's sake," muttered Tim.

They were now reaching the roadways and Paul's voice was penetrating. No one must ever know that they had actually seen the forbidden pictures, which were kept under lock and key in the Council House. One day, on some errand for Tim's father who was that year elected Chief Elder, the boys had seen just one of the old pictures. A photograph taken from the air: London in 1998. The two boys could still feel the thrill as they remembered the cloud-piercing skyscrapers joined by the cobweb tracery of bridges and runways, the colours and the sparkle on the whole scene. Just for a moment they had seen it, and no one knew. But it had been enough to fire their imaginations, and ever afterwards in their spare time they always wandered towards the no-man's land near the blue barrier.

"We should all be ashamed of ourselves, living in hovels like this," muttered Paul fiercely, "after men had built like that. And eating the muck we have to eat out of the water-tanks, tasteless, filthy stuff it is. Out there is a land where men could live the life of free men, could restock the animals from our zoos, and grow fruit and vegetables."

"We'll never do that, Paul," said

they'd die at once. Whatever can it be, Tim?"

"They do know it's electrical," Tim said. "They found that out early on. They broadcast heavy electrical charges and they cleared a few places. But it was only for a short while. It seemed that the Invaders were too numerous—they seemed to increase in some way—and anyway, the power sources couldn't keep up with it."

"It's uncanny to think that for over fifty years people have been living like this and in all that time no one has ever seen or heard anything of the Things. How did the people die, Tim?"

"Well," said Tim, "my grandfather told me that once they dragged a man back inside the Force Field. He was dead all right. There was no mark or scratch on him. Heart and

organs just stopped working as if a tap had been turned off. That's when people began to guess that these Things, these invisible Invaders, were electrical in form."

"I remember," said Paul, staring through the blue screen at the quiet jungle outside. In fifty years Britain had returned to the land of forests it had once been before men tamed it. But no animals now stalked that jungle, and no birds flew over the tall trees. "I remember how the people began to piece together the puzzle. How they realised that the first astronauts had carried the first of the Things back to Earth without being harmed, because the Invaders had no other method of transport. As soon as their job was done, those three were the first to die."

"Your father was the first to dis-

Tim despondently. "So many attempts were made, so many lives were lost in useless attempts to fight back, that now all such attempts are forbidden by law. There isn't really any penalty, just going outside would be enough."

Paul was silent for a moment. Then he stopped, turned back, put his hands on his hips, and looked back at the barrier. "Tim," he said calmly, "I'm going through the barrier tonight."

Tim didn't even look surprised. He merely grinned. "And one day pigs will fly. Come home to supper."

"Supper!" snorted Paul. "Watercress! I'd almost as soon starve. You don't think I mean it, do you, Tim? Well, I do. I've been thinking about it for a long while and tonight I'm going to do it. Someone has got to be the first."

"The first!" Tim jeered. "Why, for over twenty years after the ship landed there was scarcely a day when some brave chap didn't give his life to prove that it couldn't be done. For twenty years scientists devised every possible means of protection, and they all proved useless. What protection can you hope for now?"

"No protection at all," smiled Paul. "All attempts to go outside stopped thirty years ago, didn't they? Since then the law has been enough to keep the barriers from being crossed. I'm just going to walk through and see what happens. Coming?"

Tim looked at him in amazement.

"You're crazy. You must be stark, raving mad. You'll not take three steps before you drop dead."

"I don't think I *will* drop dead," grinned Paul. "Thirty years have passed and in all that time no one has ventured outside. I think it's time that record was broken. I'm ready to go alone, but . . ."

Tim felt cold all over. All his upbringing and education were against it. Since he had been a child it had been unthinkable that any human could live on the other side of that five-mile high field of fierce, ravening energy, the maintenance of which consumed half the power produced by the town's nuclear reactor. People had grown used to it; they scarcely thought of it. It became like the Space Barrier round Earth until the first men had shot to the Moon and then to the planets.

"Mind you," Paul went on. "I'm not taking you if you're afraid."

"I'm not afraid," burst out Tim angrily. "I'm just not a fool."

"Right, then I'm a fool," agreed Paul amiably. "But I'm going all the same, and the only thing I ask of you is that you keep it to yourself until I've gone. I'm not going to be stopped."

"I'm not a sneak," said Tim with dignity, "and to prove to you I'm not afraid I *will* come with you."

Paul laughed. "Look, don't come if you're scared, old man."

"Will you stop saying that?" Tim shouted, and a few passers-by looked at the two boys.

"Steady on, Tim," muttered Paul. "Okay, so we'll both go. When?"

"We'll do it now," said Tim fiercely. "Come on."

"Steady," Paul warned. "We can't just go like this. We've got to prepare, take food . . ."

"Now who's scared," sneered Tim.

Inside he was cold, like a statue of ice. Each step back towards the barrier caused him utter terror and his feet felt as though they were made of lead. Paul ran after him and tried to pull him back, but Tim held on grimly.

Some people from the streets ran after the boys over the grass, and Paul

saw that they were shouting and waving their hands.

"This is my last moment alive," thought Tim desperately, as he stepped through the barrier. "In an instant I'll be lying cold and still, like all those millions, years ago . . ."

It was like walking through cold curtains of tingling ice particles, ice that stung like redhot needles. It smelled cold and pungent, like ammonia. Then he was through and out into the tall grass beyond, and Paul was standing beside him. A few paces away on the other side of the barrier, a crowd of people, now fallen silent and with staring eyes, were looking at them as though they were already dead. Then, excited voices came feebly to their ears, but they could hear no words for the barrier hissed and crackled with the fierce charge of power perpetually running through it from the reactor.

"We're outside," Tim said wonderingly, "and we're still alive."

"I feel like the first man who stepped on to the Moon's surface," said Paul exultantly. "Sure, we're outside and we're alive. No man living, for a whole generation, has been outside, and no man who *ever* went outside ever lived to go back. Tim, we're pioneers! What shall we do? Where shall we go?"

"The Things," said Tim with a little shudder. "Where are they? Why haven't they attacked us?"

"We'll just be thankful that so far we're left alone," said Paul. "First things first. We're outside, and we aren't going to try to go back until we've stayed long enough to convince the others that it's safe and that they can live outside. Where shall we go?"

"Where else?" said Tim with shining eyes, his terror gone. "Where else but to London. To that city we saw in the picture."

"After fifty years of desolation," said Paul. "After fifty years in the possession of the Things. It'll be a ruin . . . it'll be, golly, we don't even know whether any of it still stands."

"Then we'll go and see," said Tim, simply, and he began to walk away from the barrier. Paul gave a chuckle, turned, and looked back at the dim forms behind the blue energy haze, and then followed.

They forgot the barrier, they forgot the little township which had been all their world all their lives. They walked into a new world, a world such as they had never dreamed existed. The trees were enormous above their heads and in places so thick they could scarcely slip between the trunks. The flowers and the grass, wild and tangled, formed an almost impenetrable jungle through which they had to force their way.

They came to a wide, open stretch of tall grassland through which a narrow river ran sparkling. On every side were uneven humps and ridges, and Paul was the first to see what the place was.

"This was a *town* once, Tim," he shouted. "Those humps are the houses, the ruins of the buildings, overgrown with the grass."

"Look over there," muttered Tim. "Something's moving, isn't it?"

They approached and saw that the movement had been the effect of the light. A small, metal framework lay on the grass. Its shape defied description; at least the boys, with their limited experience, could not attempt to describe it. Apparently made of almost incredibly fine wire, it consisted of a baffling series of whorls and spirals into which the eye looked as though peering into unfathomable depths. It looked as though it was broken, at least the glistening which had attracted them came from the jagged ends of the thing, which looked, somehow, incomplete. Paul put out a hand to touch it, then held back. They stepped back from it. There was something eerie about it.

"There's hundreds of the things about," said Tim.

Sure enough, strewn around on the grass were many of the queer, silvery wire objects, in all shapes; some were broken and flickering with a sort of weird life, and some were intact, like helices of wire that seemed to tremble on the very verge of movement.

"I'd say these were some form of invention people had made just when things were coming to an end," said Tim thoughtfully. "Some form of electrical apparatus designed to combat the invisible Invaders. Whatever they were, they failed. Let's get away from here. It's spooky."

"Soon be night-time," said Paul, looking at the sun. "Where do we sleep and what do we eat?"

"Over there looks like an orchard," Tim said, and he led the way.

They could see the outlines of the large house with the grasses grown over it like a green shroud. Scores of overgrown fruit trees stood in rows, their tops barely showing over the waving grass. The boys filled their pockets with apples. They were hard and bitter, but they would at least satisfy their hunger.

"How about digging through some of the grass and getting into one of the houses," suggested Paul.

But Tim shook his head. "I think we're scared enough as it is," he said. "Imagine what we'd find inside any of those houses. Mounds of bones, the skeletons of those who came in for protection and died where they were. We'll stay out in the open."

Paul stared doubtfully around him, but he followed Tim, and soon they found a small alcove in the grassy bank beyond the orchard. Like three

sides of a room, it had probably been an outhouse. They lay down in opposite corners and tried to still the hammering of their hearts.

The stars came out and it was so quiet that Tim could almost imagine that he could hear their hissing as they spun out there in the void. He had only the haziest ideas about the stars, but he did know what they were. It was wonderful to think that men had once flown in a ship to one of those tiny points of light, men of the same race as those few remnants which now cowered behind the Force Field Barriers.

"Look over there," whispered Paul, and, heart beating fast, Tim looked.

Two tiny points of light, steady and unwinking, stared at them from over one of the grass mounds, now darkening in the dusk. Then, as his eyes became accustomed to the gloom, more pairs of lights all fixed, unmoving, in their direction.

The two boys moved closer together and Tim's fingers dug into the grass at his feet. He was wet with cold fear, and then reason came to his aid. He gave a chuckle.

"Animals, Paul," he muttered. "Domestic animals, now wild. Wild dogs and cats, cattle and horses, pigs and sheep, all the beasts men lived with. We have them in our zoos, carefully preserved by the scientists for some future time they never speak of." His fingers had pried loose a brick, and now he lifted it in the air and hurled it at the ring of eyes. As though by magic the points of light vanished, there was a subdued chorus of yelps and squeals, and then once more that dead, velvety silence descended. "We'll sleep in relays, Paul."

They tossed, and Tim won. He threw himself down and fell asleep at once. Paul wakened him two hours later, reporting all clear, and then he, too, slept.

Tim sat staring out into the darkness, but beyond an occasional glimpse of the eyes he saw nothing. It was the most terrifying few hours in his life. With Paul asleep, he seemed to be alone, all alone, in an empty, dead world, filled with the skeletons of all the millions, long dead. He was glad when dawn came and he stood up and stretched himself. It was cold and damp and he shivered and woke Paul.

They munched their breakfast and, hard and rank as the fruit was, it was delicious compared to the manufactured food they would have had at home. They drank and washed in the river and laughed as they threw the water over themselves.

"You realise they've given us up for dead back home," said Tim.

"Not only that," Paul grinned, "but the Elders will have us listed as lawbreakers, and if we go back . . . but, golly, nobody has ever come back. If there's no danger out here, why not?"

"In our town there's no record of anyone even going through the barrier for the past twenty years," said Tim. "That's a long time."

"Don't look now, Tim," murmured Paul, "but we're not alone."

He got to his feet slowly, and they both looked at the animal which, while they had been talking, had crept almost to their feet. Black and white, its coat was shaggy and unkempt. Long, fierce teeth gleamed and as they looked, it growled deep in its throat, all its fangs gleaming. Then it made a new sound, halfway between a bark and a whimper.

"It's a *dog!*" said Tim, excitedly. "Long ago people used to keep them as pets, have them in their houses, feed them and wash them, and even have them to sleep in their beds. This one—let's try and tame it."

He put out a hand but the beast cringed backwards, growling and whining alternately.

"Let's walk away and see what it does," Paul suggested. "Don't touch it. It's wild and its bite could be poisonous."

They turned their backs on the creature and walked away. Tim looked backwards and saw it still crouched there, showing its fangs. Then it crept forward on its stomach in their direction and he could see that its nose was twitching. They walked faster and soon the animal was trotting briskly after them, but keeping a respectable distance.

They struck a roadway, a broad stretch of crumbled concrete, almost overgrown with vegetation. But its outline was visible and if it really was a road, it would lead them somewhere. At least it was better than stumbling over the grassy mounds that were everywhere in evidence and at which they couldn't help shuddering, knowing that beneath lay the whitened bones of men long dead.

"Still following," said Paul, and they halted.

The beast halted, too, and stood watching them warily but now no longer baring its fangs or growling. As long as they stood, it too stood motionless. If they moved in its direction, it backed away. When they went, it followed.

"So there is life outside," said Tim as they trudged along the track of the old roadway. "There's animals alive. I wonder how many. The books all say the animals died with the men, that the invading Things were fatal to all animal life. When men sealed themselves up behind the barriers, some animals must have survived and gone wild. Why didn't the Things find and kill them?"

Paul laughed. "That's a lot of questions. We'll never know. Let's keep it up. You realise we're heading for London?"

"How do you know?" Tim demanded, and Paul smirked.

"By the sun, stupid. Didn't you ever learn to judge directions?"

"Living as we did in a township about five square miles in area," said Tim witheringly, "it never seemed like useful knowledge. Still, I'll admit it has its uses. London!" His eyes shone. "How far?"

Paul looked embarrassed. "I didn't learn that much. But, say, just take a look behind us."

Now there was not just the one solitary dog. It had been joined by almost fifty others, who had crept after them or had slipped out of the jungle bordering the roadway. They were of all shapes and sizes and colours, unkempt and dirty, snarling and bickering among themselves but, when the two humans turned, they all stood still and stared back.

"I wish I'd learned more about the old animals," said Tim. "I'd like to be able to recognise more of them. That big one over there I do know. That was a Boxer, and look, there's a Bulldog."

"They're descendants of tame dogs," said Paul. "They haven't been very long in the wilderness. Dogs lived in men's houses so long the habit wouldn't die out as quickly as all that. We've got fifty pets, Tim.

What are we going to feed them on?"

"I don't think we need worry about that," laughed Tim. "They've lived all right so far. They'll hunt for food. See that big black brute with something red in its mouth."

"Real red meat," frowned Paul. "I've read about it. The flesh of cows and sheep. Men ate it all the time—it made them strong and big. Some men were six feet tall in those times. The tallest man in our township was just five feet. I'd like to taste real meat, Tim."

"Maybe one day you will," said Tim, his eyes shining. "If the world is free we can populate it again, we can tame the beasts . . . Let's get on, let's get to London."

They saw the wrecked rocket in the late afternoon. Its nose buried in the earth, its length towered above them like a gigantic crooked tower. They knew it from the pictures in their books. It must have plunged to earth and half buried itself. Rusted and pitted, it leaned there as a crazy monument to man's vain explorings.

"One of the exploring rockets from

Venus or Mars," whispered Tim. He whispered because he felt that it was sacred ground.

There were the bones of brave men here, men who, when Earth had fallen to silence in her death-throes, had looked up at the green Earth in the heavens, from their camps on Mars or Moon or Venus, and wondered. Then the survivors in the settlements behind the barriers had radioed them of the menace that had stricken Mother Earth almost to death. Out there these hardy men would not believe the Invading Things could be so numerous, so deadly, and so invulnerable. They would blast off for home, to the rescue. There would be very many such wrecked rockets scattered over the earth. The unknown powers of the Invaders that killed could penetrate any known metals, that had been made clear.

Soberly, the two boys turned their backs and trudged on.

It was from a hill to the north of the city that they first saw London. It was growing dusk and they stood

there and stared out and tried to hide their disappointment. Huge and massive and straggling the city must have been. But where now were its glories?

"Just a heap of ruins," said Paul dejectedly. "A far bigger one maybe, but just a heap of stones and bones." He turned away, but Tim spoke.

"Let's wait until morning," he said. "Perhaps it'll look better then. Half a century is a long time. We don't know what it looks like in sunlight. It's almost dark now. Remember the picture, Paul. It's still there, broken and ruined beneath the grass and the trees, but it's still there, you know."

That night they slept close together, and at their feet slept the little dog. The others squatted all round them and it was obvious that now these wild dogs had found men again they would not leave.

Tim was first up and he roused Paul with a wild whoop. "Come and see. Come and see London. You can almost see that old picture." He flung up his arms and shouted with glee. Paul rubbed his eyes.

It was the picture come to life. At least, their imaginations could see the picture beneath the wilderness that almost choked the ruined metropolis. Through the titanic mounds of vegetation the river Thames could be seen winding. There, amidst the ruined skyscrapers, could be seen the broken dome of old St. Paul's, wrecked and ruined, but still unmistakably St. Paul's. Of the hundreds of spidery bridges that had spanned the spaces between the towers few survived, and those few festooned and almost hidden with greenery. The many bridges of the river were all ruined and broken and the forest was encroaching more and more into that great city stricken to death.

Impatient as they had been to get to London, they were strangely hesitant now to approach still nearer. They ate more apples and sat down and made no move. Then at last Tim shook himself.

"We're scared, that's what it is," he laughed shakily. "We're scared to go down there. That's no ruined village or township. That's the capital city. If the Things conquered mankind, that's where they'd settle. But

we've *got* to go down there, Paul. If we don't, we might just as well have stayed behind the barrier."

"I'm ready," said Paul, and his voice was steady. He stroked the little dog, which now submitted to his touch, its lips quivering but the fangs never quite showing. At least they had one friend outside.

The mysterious silvery objects grew ever more numerous as they fought their way down the hill through dense vegetation, towards ruined London. They lay in mounds and heaps all over the place. The two boys threaded their way through them, eyeing them warily. These things formed the biggest mystery they had encountered in the unknown outside.

"They don't seem to have any proper shape, Tim," said Paul. "They seem to be all sorts of crazy shapes. Some seem fully formed and others look as though they've been broken in two, with parts missing. Look over there at that one just by where that brick wall ends!"

It was a small one, about half the size of most of the others. At the edge that looked as though it had been broken, a flickering and a sparkling could be seen.

Tim put his hand to his head. "Feel anything funny, Paul?" he asked in a low voice.

"Too right I do," growled Paul. "Something dashed wrong here. I'm aching in every bone. Could it be those apples? Or is there *something* out here in the outside—could the Invaders be really microbes—maybe we've only just been attacked. Tim, this is *it!* We're going to die, just like all those millions, years ago. Sorry, old man, sorry I dragged you through the barrier. I was a fool, I can see."

"Shut up," said Tim, and he set his teeth. "It's got something to do with these glittering wiry things. Look there, that small one, it's smaller than it was when we first looked at it. It's growing invisible!"

"Now talk sense, old boy," scoffed Paul. "Nothing can *become* invisible, you know that."

"The Invading Things that came from Centauri were invisible, weren't they?" Tim retorted. "No man ever saw one, at least no one lived to

describe one. These silvery things are the *Invaders*, Paul! They must be some form of electrical life about which we have no idea. You remember how strange they looked, as though when you looked into the whorls and spirals you were looking into millions of miles of space. They must live by vibrations, and their vibrations were instantly deadly to life on Earth. That one's growing dimmer, Paul. There's some left alive and at our approach . . . we can feel the deadly vibrations already. Run, Paul, run for your life."

Madly they ran down the slope, avoiding the piles of silvery things, the pack of dogs at their heels, barking and yelping as they ran. They tore along through the mounds of grass and so came to the outskirts of the city. Ahead of them the gigantic towers, draped and festooned with hanging vegetation, with broken catwalks trailing from the dizzy heights to the jungle that was encroaching year by year to cover the wonder that had once been London. In a clear

space they halted and sat down facing each other, shaking and trembling.

"The Invaders are nearly all dead at last," gasped Tim. "Imagine, after fifty years. Only those that seemed to glitter have any 'life', if you can call it life, in them. Now then, the puzzle is, what killed any of them, most of them, to judge by what we've seen? A life-form of that sort, without flesh or bones, or blood, would be practically immortal; they had no real bodies as we know it, and they needed no food but electrical energy. Something's killed them, Paul, and we've got to find out what it was. If that one we saw, and others, are reviving, perhaps the others might revive, too. Their vibrations certainly weren't fatal to plant life. We can save the people, but only if we can stop them from killing us. If we don't get back to our town, no one will ever know what we've learned. We've *got* to stop them."

Paul looked round him fearfully. The wild dogs were creeping in closer to them and as he looked he saw that

the fur was rising on their necks, and that they were all snarling and baring their fangs again. Both boys looked to where the dogs were staring and then, too, the hair on the backs of their necks stood up. A cold sweat drenched them and instinctively they moved together.

Coming out of a thicket ahead was a huge, tawny beast with a large, heavy mane of black hair round its neck. The long tail was lashing, and it was growling horribly and waving its head from side to side.

"I know what that is," said Paul through chattering teeth. "It's a lion! There's some in the zoo at Johannesburg—I heard about them once on the radio. They had circuses and menageries back in the past. There may be other wild beasts loose."

"Why here and not anywhere else?" asked Tim.

Frightened as he was, he was trying to think something out. Here where they were, there were scarcely any of the silvery things they now felt certain were the enemy Invaders. Here, too,

were animals such as they had not seen out in the countryside where the Things were plentiful. There must be something here that was death to the Invaders.

But his thoughts were interrupted by a frightful roar from the lion. It stood, not twenty feet away, roaring and lashing its tail. The dogs were snarling and yapping, but the great beast took no notice of them. Both boys faced it fearfully.

Even then Tim's eyes were roving round the scene before them. Here, where the lion had survived, if his theory was right, there must be some powerful electrical weapon, some of the radiations of which had proved fatal to the invisible Invaders, vibrating them into visibility and thus killing them. Then he saw it. A tall, tapering spire of metal, rusty in parts, erected over a vast mound of grass half a mile away. That *must* be it.

"Walk over there as though there's nothing unusual," he said, in a voice he tried to keep calm. "This lion hasn't ever seen or smelled human beings," said Tim, quickly. "If we can get to that tower I think we'll be safe."

Quietly and without haste they moved, and the beast stopped roaring. Its yellow eyes followed them as they walked, and then it, too, moved. One of the dogs, greatly daring, crept forward and sprang, snapping. The lion raised one mighty paw and knocked the dog spinning. Next instant it was surrounded by the wild dogs, all snarling and biting.

"Quick, Paul," yelled Tim. "Now's our chance."

Panting they clambered up the green mound and came to the foot of the tower. Climbing through a broken window they dropped into a dim dusty interior. The dust rose in clouds as they picked themselves up, coughing.

They went inwards through the darkness, past vast, towering masses of machinery and equipment, all silent and inert. They began to be conscious of a very faint, humming noise all around them and then ahead of them, through a broken doorway, they saw a gleam of light. It was a tiny, red gleam and it went off and on at intervals. Then a green light and then a purple, until they came to the heart of the place, a huge, dark chamber with walls of panels and switchboards and dials, with winking lights of all colours giving warning signs to——no one.

Tim breathed hard and stared at this mighty thing that they hoped would prove the salvation of the human race on Earth.

It was an hour later before they had reasoned out what it was. In the last few days before men finally gave up the struggle, this thing had been set into automatic motion, radiating its pulses round the hill on which it stood. Deep beneath would be an atomic pile, to power it for generations. Now, for fifty years, the apparatus had been radiating and the hill had proved invulnerable to the attacks of the Invisible Invaders from far Centauri.

"Fifty years!" breathed Tim. "The power could last almost for ever. But the metals, the glass and the plastic, they could break down gradually. Look, some of those dials register zero, and a lot of the light studs are blank. It's breaking down, or slowing down, and we don't know how long before it ceases altogether. Fifty whole years!"

"Where are the men who built it, Tim?" muttered Paul. "Maybe they ran out of food and ventured outside the safe radius and were killed by the Things, like that one out there was trying to kill us."

"Something like that," Tim replied. "The Things live by vibration, they are invisible when 'alive' and only become visible when 'dead'. Their vibrations kill animal life. Round here it's clean, that's why the lion survived, and there may be other beasts. The pulses from these instruments must have stopped the Invaders from growing and increasing themselves, and gradually, over the years, killed off hordes of them."

"What do we do now?" asked Paul. "If this thing is running down at last, there's nothing *we* can do about it. It's like . . . why, it's like a power-house."

"But back home, in the township, there are scientists," said Tim eagerly. "They'll be able to understand it, or parts of it at least. But we've got to get back there quickly, quicker than we came. Its pulsations aren't as strong as they were. There are Invaders out there beginning to come to 'life' again. Did you think you noticed a change in the pulsations?"

The hum that came from the banks of dials had dropped in tone for a split second, then resumed. After fifty years it was a marvel of scientific engineering that the apparatus was still functioning on automatic at all, but it was certain that already some of the separate parts were breaking down. There would come a day soon when it must all click gently to a total close-down and man's last hope would be gone.

"We owe it to the men who built this thing," said Tim, "to get back and give the news to our people. Those men died to leave this thing running in the hope that other men would find it in the future. This will set man *free*, Paul, we've got to get back quickly."

Paul was at a window and he swept away the masses of dusty cobwebs. "If there were only some horses round here," he said wistfully. "You know, those animals men used to ride. They'd get us back quickly."

"They'd be too wild for us to catch," grinned Tim. "Besides, horses wouldn't have survived, not with lions about. That lion and any other meat-eaters there are here, have had to eat to live, Paul. They can only have survived by eating each other. That means that only the fiercest and strongest would be left to breed."

"And we have no weapons," groaned Paul. "Even if we get out of this place without being eaten we can never walk back through those Things if, as you say, they're coming to 'life'."

"If any of those dogs have survived the fight with the lion," said Tim, "they'd be some protection." He peered through the glass and rubbed a place clean. "Paul, Paul, am I

dreaming or do you see what I see, coming round that grove of trees?"

Huge and massive and clumsy, the two great beasts ambled slowly along in their direction. A smaller one came after them. Two great trunks were raised in a triumphant trumpeting as the two monsters approached the snarling, yapping pack of dogs still trying to pull down the lion.

"They're *elephants*, Paul," yelled Tim. "Remember them in the books, there's none in our zoo. The largest of the animals and the one that lives longest. These two were born *before* the Invaders came. They'll remember men. Paul! They'll remember."

"There was a joke about 'elephants never forgetting'," grinned Paul. "I never thought it funny as I could never imagine an elephant. Gee, what a size! You're right, Tim. That's a male and a female—must have been in a circus, there were no wild ones in Britain."

"Elephants aren't vicious, especially circus elephants who can remember what men looked and smelled like. Come on." Tim moved.

"Hey, hey, none of that," protested the unwilling Paul.

But Tim had already broken the window and was dragging him through. Trembling, they both approached the two huge beasts; the

lion, shaking free its foes, stood roaring and snarling but not attempting to attack.

Their hearts beating rapidly, the boys went closer and the mighty beasts lowered their trunks. Tim was almost fainting from terror. To think that he was standing in front of one of these legendary monsters. He forced his mind to remember the pictures. The trunk went round the waist. Trying not to think of those massive legs that could crush the life out of anything living, Tim put out a hand and took hold of the trunk of the largest elephant. The tiny eyes stared at him as he put the trunk round his waist. He prayed it would work.

There was a pause while the eyes seemed to examine him. Then he felt the trunk tighten round him and he was lifted up. High in the air, he feared that now this monster would dash him to the ground again. No beast as huge as this could be as gentle as the stories had said.

The next moment he had been set in place and was sitting with his legs behind the large, flapping ears. Scarcely believing it was true, he looked down and saw that the other elephant had picked up a wildly-struggling Paul. Back to front, the trunk set Paul on the elephant's neck and, in spite of his terror, Tim burst out laughing, a great sobbing laugh of relief.

"Get settled, old boy," he yelled. "We're off. Kick with your feet to steer right or left. Off we go to the township to save the world."

The two titanic beasts, with their baby trotting behind, set off, and the boys yelled encouragement to each other as they went. With baffled rage the lion stared after them, and a dozen wild dogs, the survivors of the battle, trotted after them, barking and gambolling.

"Can you imagine what they'll think when we come back like this?" shouted Paul, his fear now gone.

And Tim yelled back. "We'll be the heroes of the age, Paul. We'll be in all the history books. We'll bring back proof that life can begin again in the outside and that the Earth can finally be rid of the Invisible Menace. Gee up, Jumbo."

Alone AGAINST AN ARMY

IN 507 B.C., LARS PORSENNA, ONE OF THE GREAT ETRUSCAN CHIEFTAINS, GATHERED ALL HIS FORCES TO CAPTURE ROME.

ALL THE PEOPLE OF THE SURROUNDING COUNTRYSIDE HURRIED TO TAKE REFUGE WITHIN THE MASSIVE WALLS OF THE CITY.

"QUICKLY, QUICKLY! THE ATTACKERS WILL SOON BE ON US!"

"THEY WILL SLAY AND BURN EVERYONE AND EVERYTHING IN THEIR PATH!"

"THE ETRUSCAN ADVANCE GUARD IS ON ITS WAY! CLOSE THE GATES IT'S JUST TOO BAD FOR THE LAGGARDS!"

MEANWHILE, IN THE SENATE....

"THIS IS NO TIME FOR TALK! THERE ISN'T A BOLD HEART WHICH WILL NOT FIGHT!"

"SEIZE YOUR WEAPONS AND GO TO THE CITY WALL, IN FRONT OF THE RIVER GATE!"

"THE BRIDGE MUST BE DESTROYED! THERE IS NO OTHER WAY TO SAVE THE CITY!"

"TO ARMS! TO ARMS! LARS PORSENNA IS NEAR!"

AT LAST, ALL THE BEAMS ARE LOOSENED AND THE BRIDGE SINKS INTO THE WATER WITH A RENDING CRASH.

CUT OFF FROM HIS COMRADES, AND WOUNDED IN THE THIGH, HORATIUS IS BLINDED IN ONE EYE BY A JAVELIN.

"O FATHER TIBER, TO WHOM ALL ROMANS PRAY, TO-DAY I COMMIT MY LIFE AND ARMS TO YOU!"

WITH THIS BRIEF PRAYER, HE THROWS HIMSELF INTO THE FOAMING RIVER.

THE CURRENT FLOWS SWIFTLY, AND HIS WOUNDS ARE AGONISING.

"HE IS ALIVE!"

"HELP HIM!"

"HORATIUS HAS SAVED ROME!"

HORATIUS IS GIVEN THE TITLE 'COCLES' THE ONE-EYED ONE, AND HE RECEIVES AS MANY CORNFIELDS AS TWO STRONG OXEN CAN PLOUGH FROM DAWN TO DUSK.

THE END

WE'RE ALL MAGPIES AT HEART

But for some people collecting can be a very serious hobby

Most of us collect something. There are very few people who haven't collected something or other during their lifetime, whether it be stamps, coins, autographs or cigarette cards.

These are the most common collections, but you would be surprised the strange forms that some collections take. Men have travelled all over the world in search of wishbones, mangles, typewriters, wooden legs, handcuffs and manhole covers. At a New York hobbies exhibition a man displayed a collection of nearly a hundred manhole covers, which had taken him five years to acquire. One American even brought water from the four corners of the earth, which he bottled and labelled!

There's no limit to this collection craze. One South African specialised in collecting autographs of soldiers who had won the Victoria Cross and another man from that country amassed almost a million lead soldiers. The collection of toy soldiers is a fascinating hobby and one which is practised by Peter Cushing, the famous actor and television's Sherlock Holmes.

Comedian Joe Baker is an avid collector of military insignia and his former partner, Jack Douglas, now a comedian in his own right, collects water colours and antiques.

An Eccentric Collection

But these are just everyday collecting habits compared to some of the eccentrics such as the American millionaire who hated music and refused to have a piano in his elegant mansion. His wife begged him to buy one and eventually he gave in and bought a lovely model from an antique dealer. There was no stopping him; he then bought two hundred pianos of various makes during the next two years, tracing the whole history of the piano with his collection. Eventually he had to buy two adjoining mansion houses to accommodate his pianos—yet neither he nor his wife could play a note of music!

One of the cheapest and most fascinating hobbies is collecting the humble matchbox. Collectors of matchbox labels glory in the collective term philumenists and in Britain they have their own society which regularly stages exhibitions. Matches were invented in England in 1829 by John Walker, a chemist from Stockton-on-Tees. They were called friction lights, then lucifers—immortalised in the First World War song *Pack Up Your Troubles*—followed by congreves and then safeties.

Over the years, hundreds of thousands of British matchboxes have been issued, but present day labels are drab compared to those of the last century. They bore such names as Palmer's Superior, Vesuvius, Shakespeare, Cigar Lights and Gray's Patent Improved Safety Flaming Fuses for lighting cigars or pipes in wind or rain. The Salvation Army once issued matches called Lights in Darkest England, which were labelled "Our work is for the good of humanity, will not drop or glow."

Such eminent people as the late King Chulalongkorn of Siam and King Farouk have collected matchbox labels. President Roosevelt had some private labels printed "Stolen from F. D. Roosevelt" while President Truman's personal book-match cover, gilt-marked, bore the inscription "Swiped

The Three Monarchs have a most unusual collection

Jack Douglas collects water colours and antiques

Did you know that Eric Morecambe and Ernie Wise are tegestologists?

. . . and Mike and Bernie Winters are cartophilists?

from Harry S. Truman".

Estate agents' boards have also come in for collecting by famous singer Maria Perilli, who collected those with unusual names, such as Reason and Tickle of Brighton, and well-known Midland estate agents, Doolittle and Dalley!

The late Brian Reece of PC49 fame used to collect policeman's truncheons and the famous comedian Lupino Lane, who died some years ago, was a rabdophilist—a collector of walking-sticks. The oddest item in his collection was a 100-year-old giant cabbage stalk which had hardened with age to a wood-like solidity.

Comedians and Tegestologists

A hobby of modern times is that of beer-mat collecting, known as tegestology. In Britain there is an active British Beermat Collectors' Society with its own magazine and two famous presidents in Eric Morecambe and Ernie Wise, the comedians. Eric and Ernie have hundreds of beermats in their respective homes in Harpenden and Peterborough, and they receive beermats from all over the world.

As with most collections, some beermats achieve fame through their rarity. One such specimen is the beermat printed to commemorate the feat of the famous Chung Ling Soo, the magician who caught a live bullet in his teeth, but who was later killed.

"We don't have much time for collecting beermats these days," say Eric and Ernie, "but in the early days we became quite a menace in certain well-known pubs when we went around lifting the latest specimens!"

The other well-known comedians, Mike and Bernie Winters, have a wonderful collection of cigarette cards. They're cartophilists! It's a hobby that has been going strong for years. The earliest cigarette cards can be traced to around the 1870s, when cigarettes bearing the exotic names Two Roses, Star of the World and Mayblossom contained the much sought after pasteboard cards, which then carried the pictures of such music hall stars as Marie Lloyd, Vesta Tilley and Little Tich.

An Industry from a Hobby

Although there were collectors from the moment the cards were originated, it wasn't until 1927 that cigarette card collecting was put on an organised footing. This was due to an ardent collector named Charles Lane Bagnall, who eventually formed a company which dealt solely in cigarette cards and accessories. By 1939 his stock of cards numbered 170 millions!

Up to the outbreak of the last war, in 1939, cigarette cards were works of art. Apart from sets of famous people, animals and flowers, cards provided a link with other hobbies such as coin collecting, heraldry and philately. One set, dealing with the history of cycling, formed a basis for a pageant of cycling devised by Fred Wilby, now a television director, back in 1951 during the Festival of Britain.

"We still buy cards when we can get them," say Mike and Bernie Winters. "If only they were issued now. We think they ought to be given away with cigars and tobacco, then they wouldn't encourage cigarette smoking."

Mike and Bernie have also perfected their own game using cigarette cards. Maybe one day it will be on sale in the shops!

Among entertainment personalities it falls to the Three Monarchs, those zany-harmonica-playing comedians, to possess the most unusual hobby. They collect mementoes of famous people.

Says founder member Les Henry: "It all began when I managed to obtain a ukelele which belonged to George Formby. It started the three of us off on what has proved to be an interesting, if frustrating, hobby. It's interesting, because when you get a pair of spectacles sent by Sir Alec Douglas-Home it's a real turn up for the book. Then we got a pipe from Rupert Davies, who used to play Maigret on television, and from Edward Heath we got a piece of music. Actually it was an ancient hymn.

"It's been very frustrating trying to obtain a fly-switch from Jomo Kenyatta, the African leader. We keep on trying and hope that one day it will turn up!"

These are just a few stories of collectors and collections. Whatever the subject, any collection can be absorbing . . . and it needn't be expensive. In the late thirties I began an autograph collection which had grown to well over 1,000 signatures by 1939. It was a fascinating hobby, it introduced me to lots of famous people and all it cost me was the price of a tram fare into the city.

So if you want to be a magpie, start now. You'll have a lot of fun collecting, whether it be stamps or cube sugar wrappers!

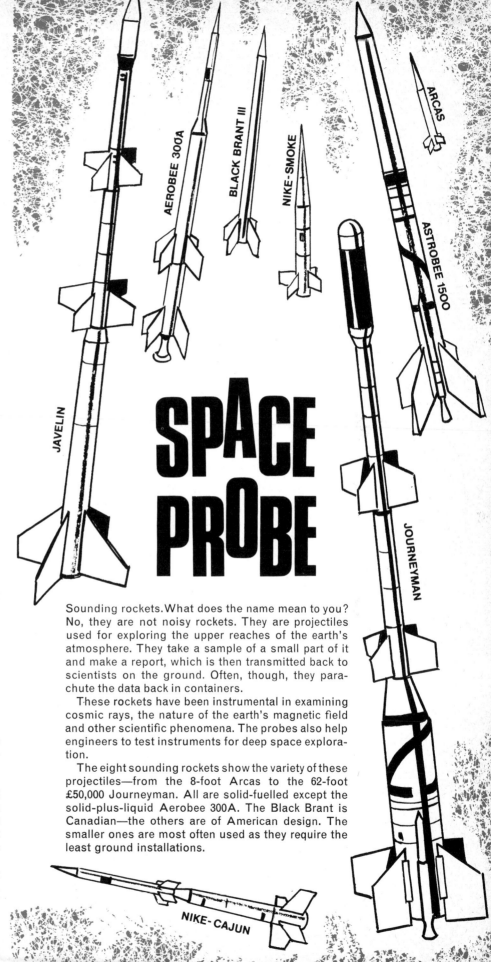

SPACE PROBE

Sounding rockets. What does the name mean to you? No, they are not noisy rockets. They are projectiles used for exploring the upper reaches of the earth's atmosphere. They take a sample of a small part of it and make a report, which is then transmitted back to scientists on the ground. Often, though, they parachute the data back in containers.

These rockets have been instrumental in examining cosmic rays, the nature of the earth's magnetic field and other scientific phenomena. The probes also help engineers to test instruments for deep space exploration.

The eight sounding rockets show the variety of these projectiles—from the 8-foot Arcas to the 62-foot £50,000 Journeyman. All are solid-fuelled except the solid-plus-liquid Aerobee 300A. The Black Brant is Canadian—the others are of American design. The smaller ones are most often used as they require the least ground installations.

Flames shoot into the sky as an English village is burnt to the ground. The screams of women and children are heard as they are carried off past the bodies of their men. Could this be England? Yes, the England of the 8th and 9th centuries when the Vikings, descending from the northern mists, plundered and killed from their longships.

The Vikings were the Nordic warrior peoples of the Scandinavian countries, Denmark, Norway and Sweden. Early writers did not distinguish from which countries the attackers came. They only cared that they did not call again. But now we can discover which areas each nation invaded.

The Danes were the Vikings who ravaged England. East Anglia, Yorkshire, Northumberland were just some of the areas that came to dread the name Viking, and prayers of the time invited God to spare them from the wrath of the Northmen.

They struck swiftly and silently... hiding their longships, plundering the countryside and then retreating before any pursuers could take revenge. In battle they seemed like wild beasts. Warriors were called *Berserkers* after a folk-lore hero who was said to fight in a frenzy. Even walled towns offered no protection as they soon found ways to reduce the defences.

INVASIONS

At first their invasions were just acts of brutality but sometimes they led to important settlements. As they became more civilised they gave up their cruel way of life and in the 800s missionaries spread the Christian faith among them, converting many away from the old gods of Thor and Odin.

In the late 800s a force of thoroughly unChristian Vikings established a base at York, conquering the surrounding countryside, and this became known as the *Danelaw*.

King Alfred, the then King of Wessex, challenged the power of the Danes-and halted their expansion in a battle in 879. But years after Alfred's death another force of Danes and Norwegians, led by Olaf Tryggvason and Sweyn Forkbeard, swept over the country. Sweyn eventually became King after the English ruler, Ethelred, fled the country. He was succeeded by Canute, famous for his forlorn attempt to control the waves; but when he died the Vikings lost control of England.

FIGHTING AND EXPLORING

Why were the Vikings so fierce? Well, primarily they just seemed to prefer a life of fighting. They even regulated their crops to fit in with their voyages. Before setting out on their raids in the spring they would plant their crops and return in the summer to harvest them. When the crops were safely gathered in they would go raiding again until winter, when the long nights would be spent playing a game similar to chess and various dice games.

Fighting often goes hand in hand with exploration ... and the Vikings were certainly explorers. They overran parts of Sicily, journeyed into Russia, took over Normandy—which got its name from them, the land of the Northmen. The Norwegian Vikings visited Scotland and Ireland, founding the city of Dublin and keeping it as their centre of power until defeated by

MEN OF THE LONGSHIPS

Brian Boru in 1014. They also reached Iceland, a comparatively easy journey when the wind was in the right quarter, catching their big square sails; from there it was just a hop to Greenland.

The Vikings reached America well before Christopher Columbus, or so the legends say, and these legends can be proved by facts.

Leif Ericsson is said to have reached the coast of America in the year 1003, in the region now called Nova Scotia. A settlement called *Vinland* was established but nobody knows exactly where. The sagas tell of trips to Vinland from Greenland and Iceland for about 12 years, but it was too far away from home for profitable settlement, and its products—soft wood and fish—were available in the homeland.

THE LONGSHIPS

The ships in which these epic journeys were made have been closely examined. It was the custom in Viking times to bury a chief in the vessel he had made famous, and two such ships have been dug up and can now be seen in an Oslo museum. These ships were shallow, about seventy feet long and sixteen feet wide. But some of the craft they constructed were as much as three hundred feet long. Propelled by oars when the sail was not in use, the ships could accommodate thirty to forty warriors.

It has been proved beyond doubt that longships could cross the Atlantic. In 1839 a group of Scandinavians built an exact copy of a longship—no shelter apart from canvas and skin awnings, certainly no engine, and a long rear oar for steering. After four weeks at sea the vessel reached Newfoundland, none the worse for wear. Even in wild seas the ship had behaved magnificently, the planking twisting and writhing frighteningly but keeping out the water.

The Vikings first sailed out of the northern mists as robbers and murderers. But the disturbances they caused often led to new ideas in the countries which suffered under them.

BEHIND THE SCENES AT ALBION

George Bartram takes a look at an ordinary day in the life of a First Division club.

The glamour appeal of soccer is often distorted in these days when professional football is becoming more and more a big business. For behind the scenes of any present-day football club there is a vast army of workers who, day in and day out, work quietly and unobtrusively to provide supporters with their ninety minutes of Saturday afternoon soccer entertainment.

Take West Bromwich Albion, for example, who have won the First Division Championship title once and the F.A. Cup five times. Their home nestles quietly on the outskirts of Birmingham and West Bromwich. But behind the redbricked walls everything is action.

The first thing that strikes you is the pressure at which all the work is done. The telephones are always ringing . . . and there is a constant stream of callers at the general office. To the uninitiated it is difficult to appreciate how all the work is coped with, let alone controlled. But it is.

The whole build-up in the club's offices—despite the tremendous hub-hub of noise and action—is aimed at the next ninety minutes of football to be staged on the ground.

There is no mystique about the workings of a football club—just a tremendous amount of hard work. It can hardly be any other way when most First Division clubs have a turnover in excess of £¾ million.

Aspiring youngsters hoping to make a career on the administrative side of soccer would do well to remember this. They see little of the club's glamour stars who, for most of the week, are away from the ground, training hard at the training grounds in Halford's Lane and Spring Road.

How the work is divided

Let's take a peep behind the scenes at an ordinary working day at West Bromwich Albion. . . .

Albion's first team group on an early morning training stint led by club trainer Stuart Williams ('T' on shorts—front row).

Broadly speaking, the club is divided into three departments. It's a sort of three ring circus, with each section working to the same aim of providing football entertainment.

There's the playing side, under manager Alan Ashman and his training staff. The administration and secretarial side, under Club secretary Alan Everiss. And finally, but by no means least, the promotion and sales side, under promotion manager Les Thorley.

And when match days come round with gates around the 30,000 plus mark, a part-time army of 700 to 800 people are employed by Albion to keep everything running smoothly.

There are the car park attendants, the programme sellers, the gatemen, the stewards, the bar staff and finally the police. All these people are essential to the stage management of big time soccer.

Manager Alan Ashman's normal working day is seldom under fourteen hours. He arrives at his comfortable, but small, office at the Hawthorns soon after 9 a.m.

After quickly dealing with the mail his telephone starts to ring. It could be any one of a host of people—from his Chief Scout Paddy Ryan, giving his latest report on a player he had been watching, to newspaper reporters enquiring about the fitness of a certain player or players.

Meanwhile, elsewhere on the ground, secretary Alan Everiss is going through the same procedure. He too could be speaking on the telephone to a director about next Saturday's travel arrangements or to the catering firm on how many steak and kidney pies could be sold on the ground for the next home fixture.

Les Thorley is also busy in his office, checking with agents of the Throstle's Pools about membership figures, or with the printers about the next home programme.

Albion's Pools are a vast organisation on their own. There are over 40,000 members, each paying a minimum of 1/- a week, and Thorley is in direct contact with the 700 or so agents who help to bring in the much-needed extra revenue.

So it goes on. Just before 10.00 a.m. Ashman is off in his car to the club's training grounds at Spring Road or Halford's Lane where he meets up with his trainers Stuart Williams, Albert McPherson and Jimmy Dunn.

They talk first about the injured players and call in club physio-

Albion's young Scottish Youth International, Asa Hartford, preparing for a training session.

Tom Jones giving treatment to another young Albion player, Lyndon Hughes.

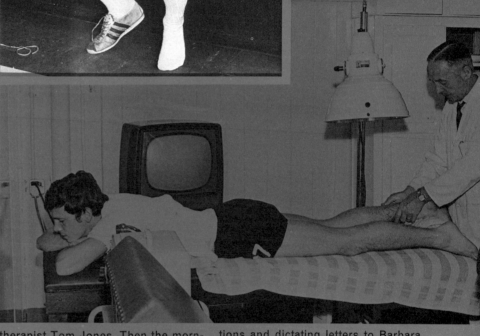

therapist Tom Jones. Then the morning's training routines are devised. They could vary from a six-mile cross-country run to a six-a-side practice match on the all-weather pitch.

Alan Ashman himself gets changed into his tracksuit and joins his players in working out new defensive techniques or a quick-strike position from a free kick situation.

Back at the Hawthorns, Mr. Everiss has just finished speaking to lighting engineers about the floodlighting for the next evening game and the Chairman Mr. Jim Gaunt arrives. . . .

He has come to put his signature to cheques which have to be paid to local traders for goods received and to speak about a new ruling from the Football League which is to be discussed at the next Board meeting.

Assistant secretary Fred Horne is sorting through postal ticket applica-

tions and dictating letters to Barbara Burkitt, one of the club's three office secretaries.

Telephonist Joyce Gulliver is dealing with a telephone booking inquiry, and at the same time attending to supporters at the enquiry desk.

Back at Spring Road the players—Albion have twenty-nine full professionals and twelve apprentice professionals—have just completed their training session and are in the showers.

Ashman climbs back into his car to return to the Hawthorns. There his secretary, Mrs. Margaret Limbrick, is waiting for dictation.

The letters completed, the telephone rings again. It's the manager of another First Division club inquiring about the availability of a player. Then the waiting newspaper men are shown in for their daily press conference.

A short break for lunch and the tempo starts up again.

It's All Go

Ashman returns to Spring Road for a training session with the reserves and 'A' team players, and to run his eye over two young trialists from Scotland who are spending a month with the club.

In the secretary's office Mr. Everiss is dictating letters to secretary Janet Willetts. These range from letters to the Football League confirming arrangements about hotel bookings to intricate points in a new contract, or a letter to the BBC about *Match of the Day*.

Chief Scout Ryan is interviewing a new scout for Northern Ireland.

Les Thorley is sending out programmes to boys all over the country, as well as dealing with youngsters coming into the Club's shop wanting rosettes and pictures.

Groundsman Stan Darby and two of his staff are repairing a faulty crush barrier at the Smethwick end of the ground.

Fred Horne is speaking to a local plumber about repairs which need carrying out to some of the club's installations.

The office secretaries are finishing off the letters, which have to be posted that night. Some of the players have come in to collect their mail.

Telephonist Joyce Gulliver is ringing Tottenham Hotspur F.C. for two tickets for tonight's game. Ashman and Ryan are going to the match to weigh up the form of Newcastle United, whom they meet in their next game.

Ashman and Ryan depart by car for White Hart Lane. Everiss is speaking to Dave Walsh, club Liaison Officer and a member of the Development Association, about the six Throstle social clubs which Albion run around the West Bromwich area.

It's 5 o'clock. The last knot of supporters are at the enquiry desk. For the office staff it's time to go home.

The phones, which have been ringing incessantly all day, are quieter now. But Mr. Everiss and his assistant Mr. Horne are still busy—preparing reports and financial accounts for the following evening's Board meeting.

Ashman and Ryan are in the Stands at White Hart Lane watching Spurs against Newcastle.

The social clubs back in West Bromwich and surrounding areas are doing a roaring trade. Everywhere

Physiotherapist Tom Jones putting Albion's England leader Jeff Astle through remedial treatment after injury.

Light-hearted training moment as Welsh comedian Stan Stennett shows Albion players some footballing tricks. Stan still plays for the TV All Stars XI.

Trainer Stuart Williams holding an inquest with first team group.

talk centres around last week's game.

It's almost time to go home. The bars in the social clubs are closing. Ashman and Ryan are returning from London in the early hours of the morning.

But there's no let up.

For in just seven hours it's time to open shop again. Work at Albion never ends. The cleaning staff are arriving at the ground to tidy the offices and repair the players' training kit for the next session.

Secretary Mr. Everiss arrives at his office. It's going to be a busy day again. All the Board reports have to be stencilled for this evening's meeting.

He is followed shortly by Manager Ashman. The telephone is ringing. This is where we came in. . . .

BENDIGO AND THE GIANT

by Tony Haynes

It was like the battle between David and Goliath all over again

Driving home that night through the darkness, the headlights of the Land Rover picking out the gum trees, Uncle Mitch suddenly turned to Jake and said, "How would you like to watch a sheep shearing contest, my boy?"

Jake stirred himself in the truck and came back to life with a jerk.

"A sheep shearing competition?" he echoed in elated tones.

"Yeah, that's right, boy, that's what I said," Uncle Mitch repeated in his flat Australian drawl.

Mitch Maloney had come to Australia as a boy of no more than ten years old. His father, who had farmed first in Ireland, then in England, had suddenly decided to emigrate. Mitch couldn't remember much about the decision. The only thing he could recall was the sea trip and all the bustle and excitement when the ship finally docked in Sydney.

The Maloneys were a stalwart bunch and although his father had little capital he soon put what he had as a down-payment on a rambling shack of a place called Coolangatta,

and hired himself a couple of Aborigine hands.

At that time there were plenty of aborigines ready to do a hard day's work for very little pay, and the two Mitch's father hired, Chulo and Ebo, were big and strong, their bodies shiny and supple. They were ready and willing to work like young bulls.

97

Thus Coolangatta in time had grown into a real sheep station in the marvellous country around the Blue Mountains, and Mitch had grown into a tough, carefree, young man with plans to extend Coolangatta even more.

"One day they'll know about us out there, Dad," he had told his father then, and his prediction had come to pass.

Now Coolangatta was one of the finest stations in New South Wales, so vast you could ride all day and never come to the end of the property line.

From being a youngster Jake had spent most of his school holidays there. Uncle Mitch had taught him to ride, sail and shoot. All these attributes were necessary out on the stations, where days could pass without seeing anyone except for the sheep and drovers. Thus Jake, too, had begun to grow up to live almost the same life as Uncle Mitch when he was a youngster.

Jake was just thirteen and had only one aim . . . to build another station like Coolangatta. Therefore whenever he had a spare moment he spent it in Uncle Mitch's company, so that he could learn everything as quickly as possible. He took such an interest that folks around almost began to think he was Mitch's son.

Jake's parents had settled in Goulburn, a fruit valley town. Goulburn was like most other New South Wales towns of its size, possessing one main street with lovely mountain views. People there were a friendly crowd who liked to celebrate, given half a chance.

Lilac Time was just one of these celebrations when everyone came in from the neighbouring farms to drink and enjoy themselves . . . but Jake had never really fitted into the way of things. He preferred to be out in the Blue Mountains at Coolangatta riding through the bush and helping the drovers to round up the straying flocks and keep them in line.

So familiar had he become with the country that he could identify every species of bush and tree in the outback for miles around.

Sadly, Ebo had died and his brother Chulo moved on, but Mitch had hired other drovers, good sun-downers who knew the outback like the backs of their weatherbeaten hands. One of these was a man of aboriginal stock called Bendigo. Bendigo could do almost anything from sheep shearing to cooking a hotpot. He and Jake had become firm friends and it was thanks to Bendigo and Uncle Mitch that Jake had learned about sheep farming so fast.

In the sheep shearing season, Bendigo often helped out when there was a man short and a hired hand was brought in for the droving. Hour after hour Jake watched his bent back as he sheared one fat, fleecy sheep after another. It was backbreaking work, starting at the bell at half-past seven in the morning, then a break for a mug of tea at ten, and then on until half-past twelve when all the shearers trooped off to the dining room for a lunch of kangaroo tail soup, steak and chips, and as often as not ice cream made by Aunt Maudie herself. Then it was back to the sheds for the afternoon's work with only a two-second interval for another mug of brew before signing off at half-past five.

In the annexe, the fleeces were thrown onto trestles and carefully examined. Then they were baled up, loaded onto trucks and shipped all over the world. Merino wool was famous throughout Australia and Jake was very proud to have seen the beginning of the story, from the moment the fleece came from the sheep's back to the time the wool

was sold in two ounce hanks in famous Sydney shops.

Bendigo had become so fast at sheep shearing that Uncle Mitch was always threatening to have a contest to decide who was the fastest shearer in New South Wales. Bendigo used to laugh, perhaps because he had enough confidence to think he could win without effort.

But, for some time, the men were so busy at Coolangatta that there wasn't time for contests or any other

amusement. All the time the property had been expanding, and consequently Uncle Mitch kept on adding to the number of sheep so that more shearers had to be brought in from all over the State to cope with the demand.

Aunt Maudie had a tough time too, with all the extra men. Every day she was churning butter or making ice cream or the Baked Alaska and peanut butter cookies Jake loved. Although she complained a bit, really

she loved it when Coolangatta was crowded and she had plenty of work on hand.

So it wasn't such a surprise when out of the blue, Uncle Mitch mentioned the sheep shearing contest.

"I'd love it," Jake said exuberantly. "When is it?"

"This coming Saturday," Uncle Mitch said, as he pulled the Land Rover up with a jerk outside Jake's father's house.

"You coming in?" Jake asked.

"No, I can't stop, if you don't mind, boy. I've got a lot on my hands at present. I'd better be getting back to see how Maudie's coping. I'll have Elliott pick you up Saturday morning, crack of dawn then, eh?" he said, slapping Jake on the back.

"Ra . . . ther," Jake enthused. "I wouldn't miss this for worlds."

"Well, it should be pretty good," Uncle Mitch said nonchalantly.

"There'll be the best in the State coming. But I reckon Bendigo can lick 'em easily."

"Too right," Jake said.

He waited until Uncle Mitch had rattled away in the Land Rover before going inside. He could hardly move for excitement, but that didn't prevent him from telling his Dad all about it.

"Guess what, Dad," he said. "Uncle Mitch's having a sheep shearing contest at last. It's on Saturday and I'm to be there at the crack of dawn to see it start."

"Good on you, boy," his father said. "Perhaps you'll learn a few tricks from Bendigo."

"I sure will," Jake said, his eyes shining.

On Saturday morning he was awakened by the laughing chorus of kookaburras. In the early dawn he pulled on his cord levis and sweater and stuck his feet into a pair of riding boots. Seconds later he was racing downstairs and climbing into the Land Rover.

Elliott was smiling all over his face, "We're all goin' take bets on Bendigo," he told him, "everyone at Coolangatta. Rumour is there's an expert coming over from Armidale but I discounted that story straight away. Then the lads think Woolangong has a strong team . . . but I reckon none of 'em will stand a chance against Bendigo."

"Too right," Jake affirmed.

Elliott swung the Land Rover round in the driveway of Coolangatta. A heat haze was rising over the Blue Mountains and from the looks of things it was going to be a scorching day, just the sort you got at that time of year. That meant the shearing sheds would be like ovens and the men perspiring with every movement.

They were met by Uncle Mitch dressed in bush shirt and trousers and riding boots, a sundowner's hat slanting over his eye. He took them straight to the kitchen where Aunt Maudie gave them giant-sized breakfasts and several mugs of tea. Then

they were all heading for the shearing sheds.

One by one the shearers from all over the State were arriving and taking a good look around. Everyone was standing about waiting with bated breath for the so called 'giant' of Armidale who was going to give Bendigo a run for his money.

It was getting on for half-past seven, time for the starting bell, when 'the giant' arrived. He was well nicknamed: a huge, scrawny fellow, six feet six inches tall, with a bearded face and bright, blueberry eyes.

He looked around at the opposition and laughed, particularly when he saw Bendigo, who was a small wisp

of a man compared with 'the giant'.

The hearts of the men of Coolangatta sank.

"Well, come on, place your bets," Elliott roared. "You're not going to be put off by this giant, are you?"

The men shifted uneasily from one foot to another.

"Well, are you?" Elliott shouted again. "Come on, you lily-livered lot," he cried heatedly. "I'll start the ball rolling by placing a fiver on Bendigo to win."

"You're chucking your money away," the giant said, throwing back his head with mirth.

"We'll see about that," Elliott roared. "Come on now. Are you with me or not? I thought you were supposed to be Bendigo's friends. Some friends!" he exclaimed contemptuously. "Why Jake here shows more support than you lot . . and he's only a kid."

Sheepishly the men of Coolangatta station began to lay their bets until everyone was queuing up with bunches of notes in their hands.

"That's better," Elliott shouted, a smile showing on his face. "I knew I could count on you."

When all the money lay in a pile, Elliott whispered to Jake. "The giant thinks because he's such a size, he's goin' to win. But mark my words, boy, by the time he's done a few sheep he won't be able to straighten up. He's too tall to keep up the pressure. Now our Bendigo's just right. You wait and see."

At half-past seven precisely the bell rang for the start of the contest.

Quick as a flash the men rushed towards the first sheep and within seconds sounds of shearing filled the sheds.

The morning flew by until by mid-morning break the giant and Bendigo were even, with twenty sheep each. The sheds were beginning to warm up as the sun started climbing in the sky.

"He'd better get into an early lead," Elliott was saying to Uncle Mitch, "before the sheds get like an oven."

"Don't worry, Elliott," Uncle Mitch said, "you can trust Bendigo to pull out all the stops."

But by lunch time, when they all trooped off to Aunt Maudie's dining room, the giant was two sheep ahead.

As they sat down to work their way through the steaks, Jake was surprised to see the giant didn't look the least bit flustered. He was tucking into the steak with great gusto, and even went so far as to have two helpings of Aunt Maudie's Baked Alaska, and topped it all off with a mug of tea, even though the sun was blazing down outside and the dining room already like a furnace.

Bendigo ate silently. He didn't even look at the giant, but as they all trooped out to the shearing sheds for the afternoon's stint, Jake saw that he didn't walk tall, like the giant.

Elliott, too, looked shattered, as if he couldn't believe his eyes.

Right on the bell the shearers moved towards the sheep. Bendigo looked quickly at the giant's score, prominently displayed on the board at the entrance to the shed for all to see.

They worked hard and ferociously, barely glancing up until the tea bell.

The giant was still in the lead with two sheep, but at least he hadn't increased his output. Jake sighed with relief.

"He'll have to slow down soon," Uncle Mitch remarked to Elliott. "That's when Bendigo will move ahead and overtake him."

"The giant still looks pretty fresh to me," Elliott observed. "He ain't showin' no signs of fatigue."

"He'd better," Uncle Mitch said between clenched teeth as the bell rang again for the last part of the contest.

"Oh, come on, Bendigo." Jake whispered beneath his breath.

Wiping the sweat from his face Bendigo caught hold of the next sheep and began seconds ahead of the giant. This was the chance he was waiting for.

If he made use of a few seconds here and there he could perhaps equalise with the giant's score. Whatever happened he just couldn't lose and

have all the men of the Coolangatta station lose a day's wages. After all, they had staked their money on him and Bendigo wasn't a man to disappoint them.

Anxiously, Jake's eyes scanned first the scoreboard and then the clock. Precious minutes were ticking away and the giant was still in the lead. Now he had settled down to a nice, easy pace, just as if he knew there was nothing to stop him from winning.

Poor Bendigo, by comparison, was hot and sticky from sweat which poured off his body onto his trousers.

"He must win, he must," Jake said, jumping up and down beside Elliott.

But from the noncommittal expression on the drover's face Jake could see that Elliott didn't think much of Bendigo's chances.

Then a strange thing happened. The giant, so confident of winning the prize, began to take things a little too easy.

Sitting squarely on his haunches

Jake had stopped watching the scoreboard, and when he next looked, he saw to his delight that Bendigo was starting to break even. He was actually beginning to level with the giant.

Half an hour to go before the end of the contest and now the giant and Bendigo were neck-to-neck.

A second later Bendigo glanced up and caught Jake's eyes. Jake gave him the thumbs-up sign.

Suddenly Bendigo realised what Jake was trying to tell him. Agile as a monkey he went forward towards the pen for his next sheep.

In all his life Jake had never seen a sheep shorn so fast and so expertly. And then Bendigo was going forward for the next and the next, while the giant still worked steadily away. The excitement in the shed knew no bounds. The atmosphere was electric

as the men, who half an hour ago had thought they had lost a day's wages, suddenly realised that Bendigo's luck had changed.

"Quiet," Uncle Mitch was prompted to shout in order not to distract the shearers.

But now the men knew without a shadow of doubt that the competition was in the bag.

All at once the bell rang and the sound of shearing stopped as if by magic.

Wearily the men dragged themselves up and staggered out of the sheds towards the comfort of Aunt Maudie's parlour, which was brimming with tea urns and sandwich cake.

Jake and Elliott scrutinised the scoreboard.

80 sheep: Bendigo
75 sheep; the giant

"Come on," Bendigo said suddenly behind them. "We're going to town to celebrate . . ." looking all at once

as fresh as a daisy. "I need a beer."

"What, take Jake into a bar?" Elliott said, genuinely surprised.

"Sure, why not?" Bendigo said, clapping an arm around Jake's shoulders as he steered him towards the Land Rover. "I reckon he's earned a coke. If it hadn't been for him giving me the Thumbs Up sign I'd have been in dead lumber," he said, winking at Elliott.

"I reckon you were fooling that giant all along, Bendigo," Elliott laughed.

The next minute, Jake was sandwiched between Bendigo and Elliott, with all the men from the Coolangatta station following behind in one of the wagons.

Already Elliott had started to go through his repertoire of songs: *The Road to Gundagai*, *Waltzing Matilda*, and so forth.

Jake had never felt so brimful of happiness. Perhaps Elliott was right when he said Bendigo had fooled them all, but there was one thing he would do, he reckoned, when he got that sheep station and became a real grazier like Uncle Mitch, and that was to hold an annual sheep shearing contest. And if Bendigo was still around he'd hire him, that was for sure.

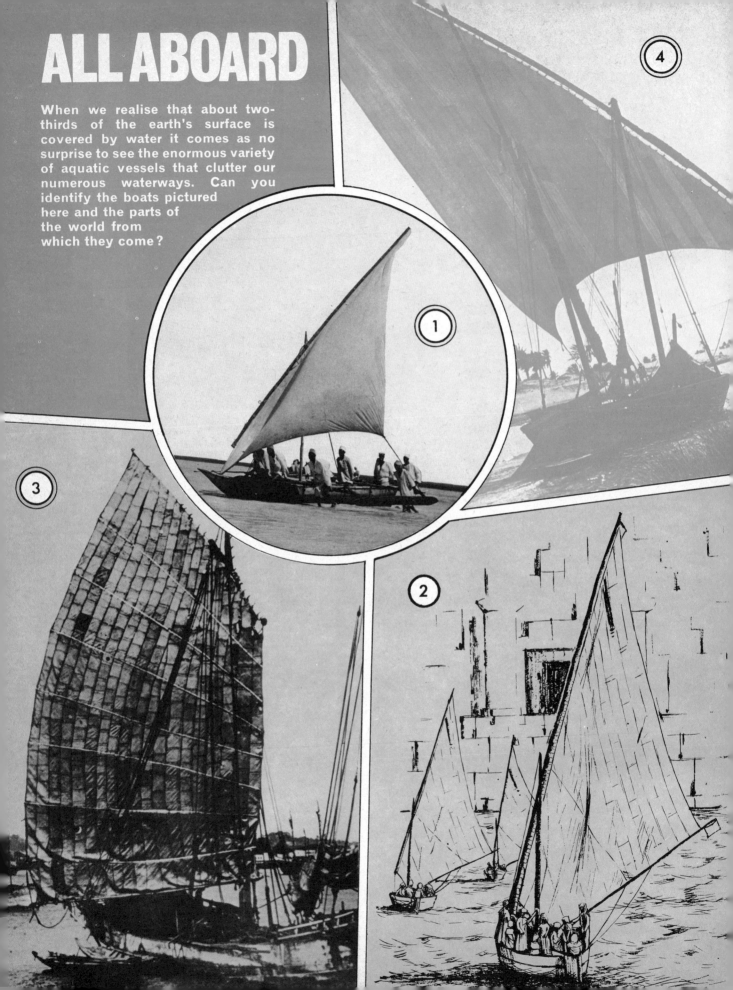

ALL ABOARD

When we realise that about two-thirds of the earth's surface is covered by water it comes as no surprise to see the enormous variety of aquatic vessels that clutter our numerous waterways. Can you identify the boats pictured here and the parts of the world from which they come?

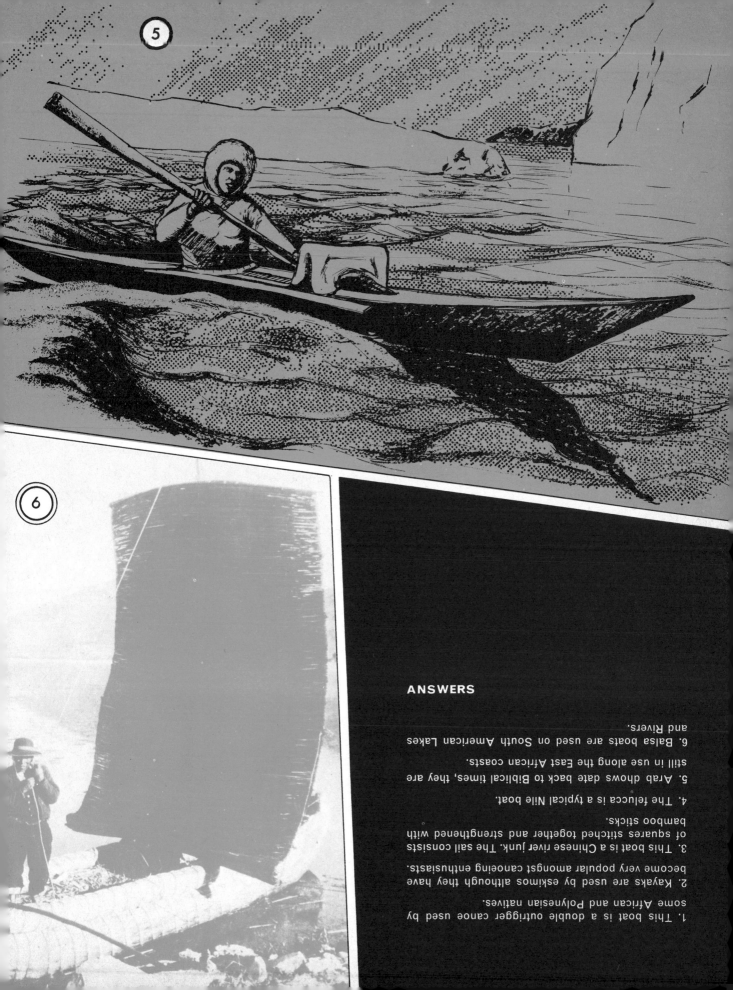

ANSWERS

1. This boat is a double outrigger canoe used by some African and Polynesian natives.

2. Kayaks are used by eskimos although they have become very popular amongst canoeing enthusiasts.

3. This boat is a Chinese river junk. The sail consists of squares stitched together and strengthened with bamboo sticks.

4. The felucca is a typical Nile boat.

5. Arab dhows date back to Biblical times, they are still in use along the East African coasts.

6. Balsa boats are used on South American Lakes and Rivers.

THE ART OF THE GLASS PAINTER

A beautiful example of a modern stained glass window

Trevor Holloway describes how a stained glass window is made

When admiring some fine example of stained glass work, you may have wondered how such beautiful windows are made. How is the glass given its glowing colours? How is the complex jigsaw of pieces built up?

The term "stained glass" as applied to many present-day coloured windows is not strictly correct, because for centuries both "stained" and "painted" glass have been employed in the making of such windows. Although the two techniques are quite distinct, a combination of both methods gives a window of greater beauty and detail, and at less cost than if only stained glass was used.

Stained glass is glass that receives its colour "in the pot" as they say in the trade. This means that there is mixed with the molten white glass a metallic oxide that stains it green, yellow, blue and so on. By adding manganese, the glass becomes violet; copper (cuprous) makes it red and cupric makes it green. For this reason self-tinted glass is referred to as pot metal.

In *painted glass*, on the other hand, the colour is not *in* the glass but *upon* it, more or less firmly attached by the action of fire. A metallic colour, which has some affinity to the glass, is used as a pigment, in much the same way as ceramic colours are used in pottery painting. The painted glass is then put into a kiln and heated to a temperature at which it is on the point of melting, and the colour actually does fuse into it. In earlier days, painted glass was used chiefly to improve the stained portions of a window; nowadays, stained glass is used to enhance the beauty of the painting.

A SIXTH-CENTURY CRAFT

The earliest known reference to the craft was made by an historian of the sixth century who recorded that coloured windows were inserted in the windows of the Church of St. Martin of Tours, in France.

The first reference to any English artist in glass concerns a man named Edward, who was appointed Master

Glazier at Windsor Castle in the year 1242. A document of the period records the rates of wages paid to craftsmen engaged in the making of coloured windows: "Those who work on the drawing, if images—1 shilling per day; for cutting and joining the glass—7 pence per day; to glazier boys [for grinding colour] 4 pence per day."

It was in the fourteenth century that a major advance was made in the art, namely, the discovery of a transparent yellow stain. It was learned that if a solution of virgin silver was applied to the glass and burnt in, it would produce a pure golden stain. This stain is quite indelible, and can vary from palest citron to deep gold. Actually, it is still the only transparent stain that glass will assimilate after manufacture.

Shortly after this discovery came another innovation of major importance. From early times glaziers had practised what was known as "flashing"—coating a white glass with ruby, or perhaps ruby over blue. It then occurred to the craftsman to etch his fine detail through this surface coating, thereby obtaining perhaps a blue pattern on a ruby field, and so on.

It was these two advances that made possible the emblazonment of heraldry upon glass. Hitherto, the cumbersome method of cutting each heraldic charge out of separate pieces of glass and then leading them together had frustrated all attempts at reproducing arms in their proper colours in a window.

A WORK OF PAINSTAKING SKILLS

Just how is a coloured window made today? The artist of the firm undertaking the work will first prepare a small-scale water-colour design of the proposed window. If the design is approved, a full-scale copy of the water colour is made in one colour only. This "cartoon", as it is called, is really a complete map, indicating all the essential features of the design.

The cartoon is then passed on to the glass-cutter. He places it down, fully opened and flat upon his bench, and then covers it with a sheet of transparent linen. Using a brush dipped in a special ink he proceeds, with infinite care, to trace the lines of the cartoon beneath, which are visible through the linen. The lines he traces will indicate the various shapes the respective pieces of glass will take, as well as the

An artist in stained glass drawing a full-size cartoon of the window

Fixing the reinforcing wires on the cutline before the pieces of glass are cut to shape

A craftsman cutting selected pieces of coloured glass to the shapes indicated on the cutline

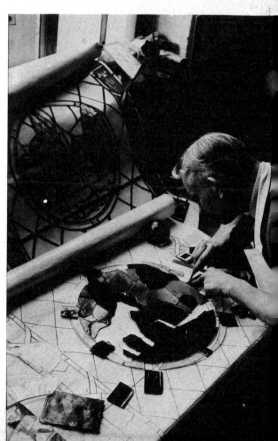

positions of the lead strips required to hold the sections of glass together. The sheet of traced linen, incidentally, is referred to as the "cutline".

The monochrome cartoon is now removed, leaving only the cutline on the bench. With the miniature water-colour beside him, the glass-cutter begins his intricate task of selecting appropriately coloured pieces of glass and cutting them to shape as indicated by the cutline. Absolute accuracy is called for, as a large window may comprise thousands of separate pieces of glass.

The work now passes to the glass-painter, an artist of high skill. First he lays the cutline on his bench, then over it lays a framed easel of plain white glass. He now assembles on the sheet of plain glass all the pieces of cut glass he has received from the glass-cutter. Slowly he builds the gigantic jigsaw together, following the lines of the cutline visible through the sheet of plain glass.

This done, the artist fixes each and every piece of shaped glass securely to the sheet of plain glass by means of a preparation of heated wax. This means that the glass easel, and the pieces of glass adhering to it, can be raised to an upright position, thus enabling the artist to set to work painting in the details of the design.

When the painting is completed, the easel is laid flat once more, the jigsaw of pieces dismantled, and the painted glass pieces are placed on shallow trays and conveyed to the kiln. Here, the heat permanently fuses the pigments with the glass.

From the kiln, the work passes to the glazier again. With the cutline again laid flat upon his bench, he takes up each piece of glass in turn and places it in its exact position. Then, with strips of lead grooved on each side to hold the glass, he fits all the pieces together, soldering all joints to keep them intact.

Finally, to make the work thoroughly sound, wind- and weatherproof, he works into the interstices of the lead and glass a cement of putty-like composition which, when it hardens, stiffens the work and renders it permanent for centuries to come. The window is then ready for dispatch and erection in its appointed place.

It is interesting to note that the colours in a window never fade, but grow richer and more sparkling with the passing of time. This is partly due to the fact that with age the glass becomes corroded by various deposits from the lead, iron or stonework in which it is set, as well as by growths of minute lichens. Curiously enough, instead of dulling the glass, these deposits enhance it with a mellow beauty.

Artists painting in the details of two windows at the stage when the pieces of glass are temporarily assembled on easels of plated glass

Crack up!

by Phillip Barratt

A wartime mystery with no reasonable explanation

K for Kenneth had copped a packet over Berlin and was legging it back for home as fast as her two remaining engines would take her—which wasn't very fast at all, under the circumstances. The two port engines had been damaged by a particularly vicious burst of flak: and it now looked as if they were both about to catch fire at any moment. But this didn't worry Davis, who was at the stick, half as much as the fact that they were losing height rapidly.

"You'll have to throw out some of the gear," he told the rest of the crew. "It's either that or baling out into the drink . . ."

The crew started jettisoning equipment as fast as they could lay their hands on the stuff. The two gunners and wireless operator seemed to think it great fun: and it was left to the observer, whom they all swore had Scotch blood in him, to show any concern in the matter. "Damn shame!" he was heard to mutter, as a particularly expensive piece of gear went whistling seawards. "Could have flogged that for a couple of quid at least!"

"You'll have to throw out still more," called Davis.

"The old kite seems to think she has a date with the North Sea!"

"She *would* have to start losing

height just when we get over the drink," cursed the rear gunner, flinging the last of his ammunition overboard.

"*Brr!*" shivered the navigator, as the icy wind tore through the plane. "It's hardly the night I should choose for a bathe."

"And me with a slow puncture in my Mae West," sighed the rear gunner, looking round for something else to jettison.

"Be in a fine mess now if a Jerry fighter decides to have a go at us," remarked the rear gunner in a far from happy tone of voice.

"Yes, it's not a very pleasant prospect, is it?" chortled the navigator, fishing for his cigarettes, and then putting them back as he remembered the petrol leaking. "On one hand we have the promise of a nice midnight bathe in the North Sea, and on the other hand we have the possibility of a rather one-sided encounter with a Jerry. The ammo has been dumped, I take it?" he ventured, passing a packet of gum round.

"Every single bit of it," growled the front gunner.

"Ah, well," grinned the navigator, "we can at least be sure it won't go off when the plane catches fire."

"Ha, ha!" grunted the observer, helping himself to two pieces of gum. "Tickle me and I'll also laugh."

"Well, Davis seems to think it funny, even if you don't," smiled the other.

"I'm sorry to disillusion you," laughed Davis, "but it wasn't what you said that struck me as funny; it was the thought of what the shopkeepers back in town will say when we don't turn up."

"Well, what will they say?" the navigator wanted to know.

"Never has so much been owed by so few!" grinned Davis.

"Maybe I'm barmy," snorted the observer, "but I fail to see how you can joke at a time like this."

The others gradually grew silent, their thoughts taking wing, leaving the aircraft behind with the speed of light so that they were now home . . . home amongst their friends, their families, parents and loved ones. How would they take it?

"Oh, what the hell!" exclaimed the front gunner suddenly jumping to his feet. "Let's throw some more gear out, or something! No point in

sitting around like a pack of maiden aunts mourning about something that hasn't happened yet."

"We're over the jolly old coast, fellers!" broke in Davis joyfully.

"Yippee!" screeched the navigator. "I knew she'd make it. We'll be having supper in Annie's Cafe yet."

"Not so fast," Davis warned him. "We're not out of the wood by a long way yet! I might as well tell you right now that we're almost out of gas."

"Whew!" whistled the navigator. "So that's how we're fixed, is it!"

"Yes," replied Davis, "that's exactly how we're fixed! She's due to stay up for another ten minutes, I reckon, so if you'll take my tip you'll bale out while the going's good."

"What about you?" the observer asked, testing the straps of his 'chute.

"I'm going to have a crack at bringing her down somewhere," Davis answered. "Call it my war effort, if you like," he grinned. "Every plane we save helps speed the end, and all that sort of thing."

"If you stay, we all stay," declared the navigator firmly.

"Don't be a fool," retorted Davis. "There's no point in all of us sticking our necks out. Now, be good chaps and bale out whilst you've still got sufficient ceiling."

"Nothing doing," they told him. "As long as there's a chance of bringing the old crate down in one piece, we stay."

"Okay," Davis sang out, "but I still think you would have been better off leaving me to bring her in on my own."

"Got any idea where we are?" asked the rear gunner.

"Only that we're somewhere over Scotland," replied the navigator, peering through the murk that enveloped the plane. "I didn't like to mention it before, but all the instruments have been shot to pieces."

"Now isn't that just too ducky," snorted the observer. "That was all we needed to make the evening perfect! How can you be sure we're over Scotland? For all you know we might be somewhere over Norway."

"We're over Scotland all right," grinned the navigator. "I smelt some haggis just as we crossed the coast."

"H'mmm," sniffed the other, "you've got a funny sense of humour all right."

"Better than having none at all," chimed in the front gunner.

"Why you—!" snorted the observer, making for him.

"Break it up, boys," called Davis, "we're coming down fast. Hold on to your hats."

The plane hit the snow-covered hillside with a rending crash, burying its nose deep into the white blanket before coming to rest. The starboard motors continued to turn for a moment or two, sending up twin fountains of feathery white spray before dying out with a choked growl.

Evans, the observer, was the first to regain consciousness. Grey dawn was creeping over the grim, bleak landscape when he reluctantly opened his eyes. He blinked painfully at the grey patch of sky that confronted him through a hole in the roof, and then endeavoured to rise, only to fall back with a groan.

Hours later, it seemed, he managed to drag himself to his feet. Swaying unsteadily, he clawed his way towards the others. They were in a pretty bad way, he found.

Help would have to be obtained, and in a hurry, too! He made them as comfortable as he could and, clambering out of what was left of the plane, staggered down the hill in search of help. Still dazed from his head injuries he did not notice the tiny trickle of smoke seeping from beneath the wreckage.

The sun came out to reveal a tiny farmhouse resting in the valley below. Stumbling and swaying like a drunken person he made his way across the snow-covered waste towards it.

The plane was already a blazing

beacon by the time he had roused the occupants of the farmhouse, and as they raced up the treacherous slopes the farmer could not help but remark that it looked as if they were going to be too late.

"We mustn't be!" cried Evans, like one demented. "We've got to get them out somehow."

As they neared the blazing plane an amazing sight met their eyes. Lying in a neat row some distance from the wreckage were the unconscious forms of the crew. But what was more amazing still was the fact that there were *no footprints in the snow*! Apart from the single erratic track left by Evans, the snow was unsullied and as smooth as glass. Nor was there any sign of another person for miles around.

Who carried the unconscious airmen from the blazing plane and where did he vanish to? And how did he accomplish the hazardous feat without leaving any trace behind him?

The solution to this extremely puzzling episode has yet to be supplied, for the crew themselves have no recollection of being dragged from the burning aircraft.

NEW COINS FOR OLD

'Money is the root of all evil' or so the song goes, and the huge number of crimes committed for money would seem to back this up. It is unlikely, however, that there was any currency in the Garden of Eden, and the problems that often surround money stem from the necessary complications that the development of any essentially simple system produces.

Before the advent of money as we know it now, business transactions were carried out by a system of exchange known as 'barter'. For instance, if a farmer with a surplus of cows found himself in need of sheep, he would exchange a number of cows for the equivalent value in sheep. Unfortunately, before such a transaction could be made, the farmer had to find someone willing to make the exchange. There might be a widespread shortage of sheep and the farmer might have to travel great distances to find a market for his cows. What was needed was something of constant value that could be exchanged in place of goods; something that was readily acceptable to everyone. A form of easily transportable currency was needed, something that could be passed from the baker to the cobbler, the cobbler to the farmer, the farmer to the blacksmith. Many different forms of currency were adopted. Some areas used objects valuable because of their usefulness, some areas used measures of precious metals. Money was born.

There was a transitional period between the disappearance of the system of direct barter and the introduction of actual coinage. During this period, coins were cast in the shape of objects previously used in direct barter. The value of these coins was directly proportional to the different values of the objects they superseded in direct barter.

This link between direct barter and coinage is most important. It is the only link between the real and the unreal in money matters. The inevitability of the origin of money is in direct contrast to the unreality that surrounds so many of the monetary figures we read today, and the difference is not only in the quantities. It can be argued that there is no difference between a coin bearing a number and a coin bearing the symbol of an object of everyday usefulness, but money is a substitute, and coins that bear such symbols remind us of this fact and of the purpose of money.

Money is important, it is probably the most powerful motivational force on earth apart from fear and love, but it is important only as a means and not as an end in itself.

Armlets and rings have been used as currency for centuries.

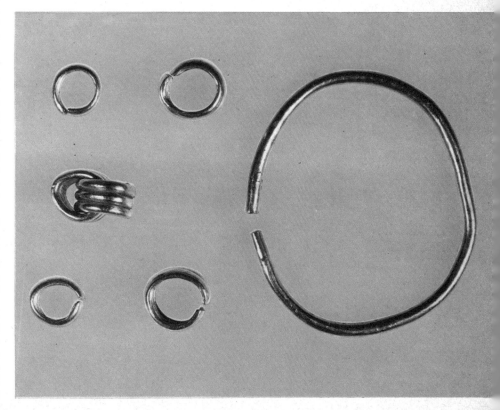

Throwing knives were used for trading in Central Africa.

An Anglo-Saxon sceat.

A long cross penny.

Spearheads and U-shaped bars were used as currency in Central Africa.

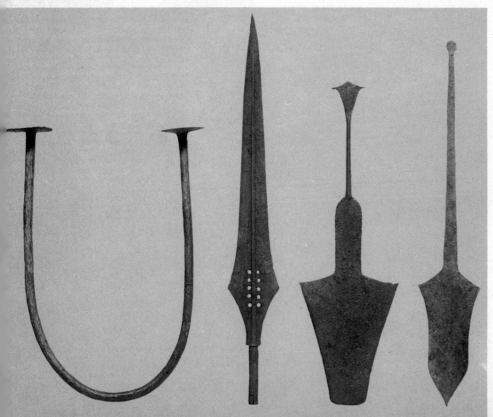

The first coins

Perhaps the earliest true coins were made by the Lydians of Asia Minor, who hammered out small bean-shaped coins on their anvils. The coins bore no design, but when the use of coins spread through Europe simple designs began to appear on the faces of coins.

Coins were introduced to Britain by migratory European tribes around the start of the first century B.C.

Roman coins were in use during the Roman occupation of Britain, but when the Romans left there was a complete collapse in the British economy, and for nearly two hundred years there was virtually no native coinage. When Britain managed to resume trade with Europe around 600 A.D., Frankish money began to find its way to Britain, and these coins were copied by Saxon workmen, and a native currency was re-established in Britain.

A good deal of the coins in Britain at this time were made of gold, and because of the shortage of gold, silver coins known as 'sceats' took their place after 700 A.D. Sceats were beautifully designed coins, but even they could not withstand the economic pressures and were soon replaced by copper coins.

Silver coins returned in the middle of the eighth century, however, when the silver penny was introduced. The silver penny was the only English coin to be struck for four centuries and during that time, if smaller denominations were needed, it was the usual practice to cut pennies into the amounts required.

Edward I introduced halfpennies and farthings in 1272, and Edward III gave us the groat and the half-groat. After Edward III's reign, English coins and the values at which they circulated underwent innumerable changes until the last major change in our coinage—the issue of the twelve-sided three-penny piece in 1937.

Now we must prepare ourselves for the biggest change there has ever been in the history of British coinage.

An ancient currency bar.

Our new decimal coinage

The United Kingdom will change over to decimal currency on Monday, February 15th 1971, and the changeover will affect us all in a number of ways. In spite of the obvious confusion that the changeover will bring, it is hoped that the new system will streamline Britain's export industry and eventually help to raise the standard of living in Britain. It is hoped that the system will also help towards harmony in Europe and ultimately the world.

There have been a number of objections to the changeover, however, and we shall have to wait a long time before we can begin to measure the advantages and disadvantages of the new system. If the changeover is unsuccessful, it will have been an expensive mistake—the estimated cost is £128,000,000.

At present we use three units to measure money values; the pound, the shilling and the penny. The decimal system has only two units, the pound and the new penny. The pound will retain the symbol £ as a means of identification, but new pence will not be represented by the letter d, which has been with us since the eighth century. The abbreviation for new pence will be p and the pounds and the new pence will be separated by a decimal point. The new halfpenny will be expressed as a vulgar fraction ½p. Under this system we will see two possible ways of expressing amounts of money as is shown below:

The new decimal coins.
Five new pence is worth 1/-.

The 50p coin which takes
the place of the 10/- note.

1st	2nd
£50	£50·00
£2	£2·00
25p	£0·25
2½p	£0·02½

There are seven £.s.d. coins in general use. The decimal system has six coins: three bronze 'copper' coins and three cupro-nickel or 'silver' coins. The three 'copper' coins (½p, 1p and 2p) are worth 1·2d, 2·4d and 4·8d respectively. The 'silver' coins—5p, 10p and 50p—are worth 1s, 2s and 10s respectively. The 5p and 10p coins are the same weight and size as the shilling and the florin, and the 50p—a seven-sided coin—is somewhere between the florin and half-crown in size.

The changeover to decimal currency has to be staggered to lessen the confusion that must arise from the transition.

This is how the changeover was planned:

Spring 1968:
5p and 10p coins came into circulation.
August 1969:
The ½d ceased to be legal tender.
October 1969:
50p coin came into circulation.
January 1970:
The half-crown ceased to be legal tender.
February 1971:
½p, 1p and 2p coins come into circulation.

This programme raises several points. After the introduction of ½p, 1p and 2p coins, there will be a transitional period when shops and offices will still use the £.s.d. system when necessary, but although the penny, threepenny bit and sixpenny piece will continue to circulate, they will decline in usefulness and will eventually cease to be legal tender.

The substitution of the 50p coin for the ten shilling note is not a necessary part of the changeover, and was undertaken for economic reasons, as the average life of the ten shilling note is only four to five months.

Because the new system is based on the pound, it is not necessary to replace the £1, £5 and £10 notes now in circulation. They will eventually be replaced by smaller notes of new designs, but this change will not begin until 1972.

£128,000,000 is a lot of money. Some would say that it is too much money to pay for decimalisation. Others might say that the changeover is a good investment. However you look at it, it's only money.

Reproduced by permission of the Central Office of Information, London.

SPORTS on STAMPS

**Ian F. Finlay
discusses a particular
branch of
stamp collecting**

The world's first adhesive stamp was the now famous Penny Black, issued by Great Britain on 6th May 1840. Since then, almost every country in the world has issued its own stamps, and the total number of different stamps to have appeared since that day early in May 1840 is well over 140,000. In the early days, people used to collect stamps from the whole world.

With the great increase in stamps issued, this was no longer possible or practicable, so that a choice had to be made. Some people chose to collect the stamps of a certain country or continent, others those of a given period, while others chose stamps showing a certain subject. There are now stamps showing almost everything under the sun—and even the surface of the moon. Amongst the varied subjects are several hundred connected with sports, which are very popular with collectors. We are going to look at some of them now, since they are sure to appeal to you, too.

The Olympic Games
The first stamps showing sports were in a set issued by Greece in 1896, when the modern Olympic Games were held for the first time, in Athens. These Greek stamps showed some of the sports played in ancient Greece, and they are now quite rare and valuable.

Stamps have been issued for most of the modern Olympic Games, which are usually held every four years, on each occasion in a different country. The next are to be held in Munich in West Germany in 1972, the last having been in Mexico in 1968.

One example of such a stamp, showing high jumping, comes from a set issued by the Rwanda Republic in Central Africa for the 1964 Olympic Games, held in Tokyo.

These Olympic Games stamps usually show sports, but some also show the grounds where the games are held. The Olympic Games have been held in England twice, first in 1908, and the second—the first Games after the War —in 1948. Four special stamps were issued by Great Britain for the 1948 games. They are not very interesting.

Of greater interest to us is a stamp issued by Monaco, a small country on the Mediterranean coast, in 1963. It shows a view of Wembley Stadium in London. The stamp was issued to mark the centenary of the Football Association.

Of interest, too, is the set issued by Great Britain in 1966 when the final of the World Football Competition was held at Wembley and won by Great Britain. One of the stamps in the set was issued later with an overprint stating "England Winners".

Other Games and Sports
It is sometimes difficult to make a distinction between a game and a sport. Table tennis, which used to be called ping-pong, from the sound made by the ball, is usually considered to be a game. It is, however, a very popular and skilful game. There is a beautifully coloured stamp issued in 1961 by the People's Republic of China showing a table-tennis bat and ball and a Chinese temple. It was issued for the world table-tennis championships held in Peking, the capital of China.

Cricket too, is usually looked on as a game. Although it is very popular in England, Australia, New Zealand, India, Pakistan, South Africa and the West Indies, there are very few stamps showing it. Guyana, on the northern coast of South America, did issue a set in 1969 to mark the M.C.C.'s West Indies tour. Each of the stamps shows an important part of cricket: wicket-keeping, batting and bowling. The bright blue sky is a change from the grey ones we often have here in England for cricket matches!

Winter sports are becoming more and more popular these days, and the Winter Olympics are now a regular part of the world sporting calendar. In 1964 they were held at Innsbruck in western Austria, and one of the stamps issued by Austria to mark the event shows a man skiing.

Boxing is another very popular sport in most parts of the world, and it is shown on a number of stamps. One of these comes from a set issued by Dahomey, a small country on the west coast of Africa, for the Dakar Games in 1963.

Sports played in or on the water are also very popular. There is an interesting stamp in a set issued by Panama in Central America in 1964, showing underwater fishing.

A stamp from a Roumanian set of 1962, devoted to boating and sailing, shows a man in a kayak, a type of one-man canoe used mainly by the Eskimos and Greenlanders. You will also remember that Great Britain issued a stamp in 1967 when Sir Francis Chichester made his world voyage in Gipsy Moth IV.

Moving from the water back to land, the small country of San Marino, near the east coast of Italy, brought out an interesting set in 1962, showing some of the activities in mountaineering. One of the stamps shows a man 'roping down', that is to say making his way down a very steep face of rock using his feet and a length of rope.

Another strenuous activity is weight-lifting, and an example of it can be seen on a stamp from China issued in 1965 from a National Games set. Dubai, a small state on the Persian Gulf, issued a set of large stamps for the 1964 Tokyo Olympic Games. One of them shows a man doing gymnastic exercises. This is something that looks easy until you try it for yourself!

A very long and narrow stamp from Poland, issued in 1962, shows a large number of cyclists in the International Peace Cycle Race. Cycling is also a very popular world sport.

Every Stamp Tells a Story
We could go on and on, listing different stamps from all parts of the world showing all kinds of sports and games. You will thus see that there is much that you can learn from stamps. This is the wonderful thing about them. Each stamp shows something and each stamp has, in this way, a story behind it. By collecting stamps you can learn as you save. Every time you get a new stamp, you should try to find out as much about it as you can. What country does it come from, where is the country, when was the stamp issued, why was it issued, what does it show? In this way, you will learn a lot and also get more pleasure from your collection.

If you decide to collect stamps showing sports and games, there are one or two special books describing stamps of this type. You will probably find that your Public Library has them.

You will have to decide for yourself how you are going to arrange the stamps. Perhaps you will put them according to countries or according to the sports they show. That is another exciting thing about stamps. You can use your own imagination in the way you set them out.

Whatever you do, I am sure you will find it interesting and enjoyable, since stamp collecting is a fine hobby.

HEADACHE ON THE HOOF

A Scouting Adventure by Kevin McGarry

A curlew called far off across the Yorkshire moors. It was a lonely sound. But Dusty Miller didn't even hear it. He sat barechested in the hot sun outside the stable buildings and quoted poetry:

Great is the sun, and wide he goes
Through empty heaven without repose;
And in the blue and glowing days
More thick than rain he showers his
rays.

Above the hills, along the blue . . .

"Hey, Tug, what comes next?" He appealed to his friend, known around the village as Tugboat.

"It sounds like a horse." Tug was kneeling on the grass with one ear to the ground.

"Naw! That doesn't rhyme."

"Shut up!" Tug turned his head and tried the other ear on the ground.

"But, Tug, I've got to learn this poem before we go back to school," said Dusty.

His pal looked up in triumph. "It *is* a horse. I can hear it walking with my ear to the ground like an Indian."

"What's biting you? A horse walking with his ear to the ground like an Indian."

"It's in Spotted Dick's garden." Tug got up with unusual speed. "We'd better see about it, in case he is away."

Dusty rose reluctantly, and followed Tug round the stables. He was never too fond of going past the empty stalls. Now the farm had gone completely mechanised, the only use

for the stables was storing odds and ends.

They climbed the fence, edged through some shrubbery and came upon Mr. Spodick digging in a flower bed. He looked up and smiled in his usual friendly way.

"I thought I heard a horse walking," Tug explained.

"What you heard was probably Sir Walter Scott," said Mr. Spodick, and went on digging.

"I—" Tug paused and blinked. "I thought it was a horse."

"Sir Walter seemed restless, so I tethered him behind the barn," Mr. Spodick said casually.

The two boys went round the barn to look. There, walking round the small paddock, was a fat little horse

that looked lonesome. He pricked up his ears with a pleasant expression.

"This is Sir Walter Scott," said Mr. Spodick, coming around the corner of the barn. "He belongs to my sister, who has left him with me during her holiday."

"Oh great! I love horses." Tug went over and stroked Sir Walter's neck. "D'you mind if I come over and see him once in a while?"

"Come anytime," Mr. Spodick said eagerly. "You may take full charge of him, if you wish."

"Tug doesn't love him that much," Dusty said.

"Yes, I do, too!" Tug spoke warmly. "I'll be tickled pink to look after him . . . Dusty, go and bring him a pail of water."

"Me!" Dusty snorted. "He's not my baby."

"Run along and get the water— that is, if you want some help with your maths tonight," Tug said sweetly.

"You can't kick me around that way," Dusty cried. "I'll get the water because I like the horse, not because you told me to." He walked away with an independent air.

Mr. Spodick leaned against the barn wall in search of some shade. He mopped his red face with a large coloured handkerchief. "My goodness! How hot it is! I do hope it rains soon." He looked around at his lawn and flower-beds with a mournful shake of his head. "This drought has played havoc with the grass and

flowers," he sighed. "And my well has run dry, like so many round here. So I can't water the plants."

"Where do you get your water from then?" asked Tug.

"From the farm," said Mr. Spodick. "But even there it takes so long to fill a bucket."

"They've had to put up standpipes on the street corners in the village," said Tug. "D'you think it'll ever rain again? Maybe these moonshots have kind of upset the weather."

The man chuckled. He fanned himself with his old felt hat. "Maybe you're right. I've almost forgotten when it rained last."

They chatted some more. Then the horse threw up its head and whickered. They turned to see Dusty coming round the barn. The bucket in his hand was only half full of water.

"It's all I could get," he snorted. "You'd have to stand all day at that tap to get a bucket full of water."

"It isn't much, is it?" Tug frowned, and reached out a hand for the bucket.

"Oh, no, you don't!" Dusty wasn't to be denied the pleasure of watering the horse. "I brought it. I give it to him!"

Sir Walter Scott was straining at the tethering-rope. He almost knocked the bucket out of Dusty's hand as the boy came towards him.

"Hey! Take it easy! You must be awful thirsty," said Dusty.

They watched the horse greedily sucking up every last drop of the water. "Ah, that seems to be why Sir Walter is so restless. He's thirsty!" said Mr. Spodick.

"Oh yes. I knew that," said Tug, with a casual air of superiority. "I bet Sir Walter isn't used to dry weather."

Mr. Spodick gave him an appraising nod. "How perceptive of you, my boy. It so happens you're quite right. My sister lives in the Lake District and, as you probably know from school, they have about eighty inches of rain there in a year. So I would definitely call Sir Walter a water-horse, wouldn't you?"

The boys agreed. By this time the horse had drunk the bucket dry, and tossed it aside with a flick of his head.

"He wants more," said the expert, glancing meaningly at his pal.

"Is that so?" Dusty gave back a hard stare. "Then trot off and get some, vet."

Tug was searching around for a scathing remark when Mr. Spodick

hitched up his old gardening pants and said: "Well, I must get back to my flower beds."

As he disappeared round the barn, Dusty was retrieving the bucket. He handed it to Tug. "Okay. Go and take your turn at that mouldy old tap," he invited.

"I've got a better idea," announced Tug. "We'll unhitch Sir Walter and take him down Top Moor Hollow to Upghyll Brook. There should be enough water in it for him to have a proper drink."

So they set off, with Tug leading the horse by the halter. The sun was scorching on the open moors, but there was a pleasant Pennine breeze to make it bearable.

The two boys reached the ridge from which the moor sloped down steeply towards Upghyll Brook. It was screened from them by a dry-

stone wall and some low bushes. But apparently the scent of water was not screened from Sir Walter. He flung up his head with a sudden whinny, and the next moment he bounded forward.

"Hi! Stop it, you dumb horse!" yelled Tug.

He was hanging onto the halter, being pulled along behind his charge at top speed. His bare brown legs moved so fast they became a bit blurred to Dusty, who ran behind. "Let go the halter, you ass!" howled Dusty, as Sir Walter streaked straight for the stone wall.

Tug got the message just in time. He let go and went sprawling, just as the thirsty horse launched himself over wall and bushes.

As Dusty ran to help his pal to his feet, there was a sudden commotion from behind the hedge . . ."Hey! Our water!" It was a boy's voice. And another joined in: "Chase the brute away! He'll have it all drunk."

Tug and Dusty scrambled to the top of the wall. Below them, on a level patch above the brook, they saw a small neat camp site. There were four green tents, and a small white one, pitched in a semi-circle. There was a kitchen area, enclosed by white string, and it contained a woodcraft table and several nifty gadgets for holding utensils, made out of branches.

"They're Scouts," declared Tug.

They could see three angry boys racing towards the spot where Sir Walter Scott was drinking from a canvas water-bucket. One of them, who had a shock of red hair, was brandishing a Scout-pole.

"Hey!" yelled Tug, almost falling from the wall. "Don't hit him! He's only thirsty."

The Scouts halted and turned to the intruders.

Tug and Dusty scrambled down from the wall and came running towards the camp. It was too late to do anything about the water-horse. He was licking his dripping lips. Then he ambled away towards the brook, trampling the canvas bucket underfoot.

"Is he your horse?" asked Red Head belligerently.

Tug shook his head. "Not exactly,"

he said. "But I'm in charge of him. And he's a kinda thirsty horse."

"You don't say!" a tubby Scout said with heavy sarcasm.

"We're sorry he drank your water," said Dusty. "We were bringing him to the brook for a drink."

"Ha! Hear that, Eddy?" Red Head gave a mirthless laugh, and turned to the third Scout.

Eddy seemed to be the least upset of the Scouts. He wore his uniform shirt, and Tug could see that he had Patrol Leader's tapes on his pocket.

"He won't get much to drink from the brook," said Eddy. He gave a pleasant grin and motioned the two strangers to follow him. They found Sir Walter standing sadly by the banks of an almost dried-up bed, down which Upghyll Brook had dallied without pause for as long as the village boys could remember.

"Wow!" said Dusty. "Some drought . . . We've never known this to happen."

They turned back towards the camp site. "How are you managing for water then?" asked Tug.

"We've got to lug it from that farm near the road," said the tubby Scout. He picked up the trampled canvas-bucket and peered mournfully inside it.

"Sorry!" said Tug.

Eddy waved his hand. "Not to worry," he said. "Bill and Bingo are bringing up some more water right now . . . We're the Plover Patrol. I'm Eddy Cooney, Patrol Leader, and this is Tubby and Mick."

Tug introduced Dusty and himself. Then he told how he came to be in charge of Sir Walter Scott. He also explained that he was a water-horse.

"I wonder if it will ever rain again," sighed Tubby. He lay back on the grass and looked into the cloudless sky.

"Didn't they use to try and *make* it rain—in places like Arizona, I mean," remarked Dusty.

Mick, who was squatting by the fire-trench, adding sticks to the blaze, looked up quickly. "Hey! That's a great idea," he said. "Why don't we try the Hopi Indian Snake Dance."

"The what?" The others all spoke together.

Mick ran a bony hand through his red thatch. "Ignorant lot, aren't you?" he commented cheerfully. "Never mind. Leave it to your blood-brother here. I'll give you a little talk on the Snake Dance, and then we'll try it out."

"Why, what do *you* know about Indian dances," said Tubby rudely.

"Me rain-in-the-face Indian," chanted Mick. "Snake dance is colourful ritual for the rain gods."

"Phooey!" said Tubby.

"How!" grunted Mick.

Half an hour later the Plover Patrol and their visitors were drinking tea and eating baked beans around the camp fire.

Sir Walter Scott was tied up out of

reach of the water-buckets which Bill and Bingo had just carried up from the farm.

Mick did his bit about the Hopi Indian Snake Dance. He explained about the costumes they would need. Tug and Dusty promised to get what they could from home and bring it down that same evening.

So it was that as the six o'clock news reader was talking about the forty-fourth day of the Drought on Eddy's transistor, the patrol and their new friends got ready for the Snake Dance.

Tubby and Mick, with harmonicas, were the orchestra. This duet began making rapid and futile passes at a little tune called *Singing in the Rain*. At that, they were closer to the tune than the chorus, whose vocal efforts sounded like an alley full of wet cats.

But the hideous sound effects were nothing compared to the sight that met the eye. Not since Noah's Ark had anyone been so well prepared for rain. Tug was wearing hip-length fishing waders and was waving a big

black umbrella overhead. The only visible portions of Bingo were his head and hands, sticking through holes in a table-sized piece of old yellow oilcloth.

Out in front of the orchestra was the chorus. It was out of line, out of step and out of tune. Apparently none of this mattered, for it was definitely not out of costume.

It was next to impossible to see Dusty. He was almost hidden from view by a huge army poncho-cape. At times this tent-like shape appeared to be doing kick-steps with the rest of the chorus.

Eddy wore a sandwich sign that read "Slippery When Wet".

And Bill had the canvas-bucket dangling from his belt, along with a mop and a weather-vane.

And of course everyone had chicken feathers stuck in his hair and streaks of bright red paint on his face.

The mournful curlew, who was accustomed to doing his saddest and loneliest calls across the moors at this hour, gave up in disgust at the yipping and yowling.

Mick stopped blowing into his harmonica, and capered up and down in the role of witch-doctor.

Suddenly, with a dramatic howl and a Hollywood gesture, he brought the ceremony to a climax. They all crouched, grinning and watching.

Mick waved a rubber snake in each hand and appealed to the sky. "Ungoo—Magoo—Umalip—Drip drip!"

They all cheered like mad.

"Hey, Chief Rain-in-the-Face," called Tug, "what's the prediction?"

Mick squinted up at the cloudless sky. "Rain! Heap big rain!"

Everyone cheered wildly. After that they all climbed out of their costumes, and cleaned up before sitting down to a 'heap-big feast'—as Tubby called the buffet tea he had prepared. They were in the middle of it when they heard voices approaching on the other side of the wall.

"Sounds like girls," said Dusty.

"So it does. Listen to them giggle," added Bingo.

A head of chestnut curls appeared over the top of the wall. "Oh look, Miss Holmes. There's a horse over here," said a shrill voice.

Sir Walter Scott raised his head and whinnied. That brought three more girlish heads into view. "Ooh, some boys too," giggled one.

"It's a mirage—part of the drought," exclaimed Bill, the ever-hopeful Romeo. "We're stranded in the desert with beautiful damsels."

"Young man, this is the art class from the girls' school." The speaker was an older woman, rather severe-looking, who now prepared to climb the wall. "Come along, girls. We'll cross this dry ditch and climb the moors over there to sketch the sunset."

When the teacher and her giggling charges had scaled the wall, Tug rose to his feet and gave them a bow.

"I wouldn't cross this dry ditch at this time of the evening," he advised.

"Why not?" asked the woman sharply.

"Well, it happens to be the bed of Upghyll Brook," said Tug. "And if it rains these moorland becks can flood in a big hurry."

"That dry ditch have water in it!" laughed one of the girls.

"Well, it didn't get washed that deep with ginger beer," Dusty grinned. "But Tug's right. It looks like rain, and it would be better to stay on this side of the brook."

"Thank you!" the instructor said, "but dry ditches don't frighten us."

The boys watched the art class cross the dried out stream-bed and vanish over a rise in the moor.

"What did you mean about it looking like rain," asked Eddy, turning to Dusty.

The other pointed away to the south-west. While they had been busy talking, the first dark clouds had begun to pile up.

Mike whistled. "Hey, maybe that Hopi Indian Snake Dance has done the trick," he said.

Eddy rose to his feet. "You may be right," he said. "Anyway, we'd better be on the safe side and dig some rain-trenches around the tents."

That job took them the best part of half an hour. As they finished the rain came. There was a roar of wind, and a beating, driving rain. They were drenched through before they could dive into the tents.

"So much for the drought," commented Tug, as they crouched on the sleeping-bags and listened to the rain beating a tattoo on the canvas.

"Hey, I bet Sir Walter Scott is loving this!" exclaimed Dusty. He peered out of the tent-flap. The others craned over his shoulder. The horse stood happily cropping the grass, his ears quivering with pleasure as the rain poured down his gleaming flanks.

"You ought to call him Sir *Water* Scott," quipped Bingo.

"Hey, listen!" cried Mick from the next tent. "The brook is coming to life."

They fell silent, and heard a low rumble that swelled into an angry roar. They looked down towards the dry bed of the brook, and saw a two-foot crest of water racing down.

"It'll be a torrent in no time—just as I told that woman," said Tug.

Eddy grew suddenly alert. "Hey, I was forgetting them," he said. "Hadn't we better see where they are?"

"Maybe we ought," agreed Bill. "If they try to cross back to this side while it's in flood—"

They emerged from the tents, pulling on their anoraks and waterproof capes. They went towards Upghyll Brook.

"Holy snake dance! It's a thundering great river!" gasped Tubby.

The cloudburst was raising the level of the moorland stream every minute. It boiled with the fury of a pent-up cascade.

"Listen!" cried Eddy, raising his hand.

They strained their ears. Between

lulls in the wind there was unmistakably the sound of a feminine voice yelling for help.

"They're in trouble," exclaimed Tubby.

"Look, there's the teacher," said Mick, pointing across the foaming brook.

The woman looked bedraggled and desperate. "One of my girls has twisted her ankle!" she yelled. "Can we get across anywhere? My car—it's parked over there."

Tug looked at the water. It had risen a foot or so since they had been standing on the banks. "Not a hope of crossing," he said.

Then Dusty dug him in the ribs. "What about the water-horse?"

"Hey—that's it!" exclaimed Eddy. "You could ride him across . . . Bring 'em back a couple at a time, riding behind you."

Tug was already running to where Sir Walter still grazed. He signalled the Scouts to give him a leg-up.

Sir Walter looked up, surprised and startled to find someone on his back. For a moment his ears went back, as if he resented it. Then Tug began to pat his soaking mane, and talk quietly to him.

"He's doing it!" exulted Dusty. And sure enough, the horse made straight for the brook.

They raised a cheer as the rider guided his steed up the far bank, towards the woman.

The rescue operation went without a hitch. The bedraggled girls were ferried safely across the torrent, and then led to the teacher's car, while the one with the twisted ankle was taken on the horse's broad back.

When the car had driven away, the Scouts and their friends looked in admiration at Sir Walter Scott. He seemed to have an idea that he was the star of the whole adventure, for he raised his head and whinnied at them.

"Wonder what he's saying?" said Tug.

"Well, at least he is not asking for a drink any more," said Dusty.

The Jack Horner of the nursery rhyme actually lived. He was Thomas Horner, steward to the Abbot of Glastonbury. He was told to deliver a pie to the king containing the deeds to twelve manors, but on the way he managed to extract one of the deeds for himself.

Under the system of purchasing commissions in the old British Army, boys often served as officers. There was a schoolboy officer in the Duke of Wellington's Regiment.

Wife-selling was not uncommon at one time. A newspaper of 1729 reported that a man called Everet sold his wife for a three-shilling bowl of punch. At Worcester, about a hundred years ago, a man sold his wife for a shilling and a quart of ale.

The exclamation 'Whoa,' often used to stop a horse, is a corruption of the cry 'Ho' which ended tournaments between knights of old.

A man was once literally saved by the bell. A sentry on duty at Windsor Castle was charged with sleeping on duty, but he said that this was impossible because he claimed that he heard St Paul's bell strike 13 that night. He was proved correct and escaped with his life.

In ancient times messages were relayed in odd ways. In Persia men would stand at calling posts set at intervals between towns and cry their messages in shrill voices.